the world of automobiles

An Illustrated Encyclopedia of the Motor Car

COLUMBIA HOUSE/New York

Executive Editor: Ian Ward
Editorial Director: Brian Innes
Assistant Editors: Laurie Caddell
Charles Merullo
Mike Winfield
Art Editor: David Goodman
Art Assistant: John Heritage
Picture Editor: Mirco Decet
Cover Design: Harry W. Fass
Production Manager: Warren Bright

contributors
ALAN BAKER: Ventilation
DAVID BURGESS WISE:
Unic
Vale
Vanden Plas
Vanderbilt Cup
Varzi
Veteran and Vintage
Vinot
Voisin
Voiturette Racing
Vulcan
Wagner
LAURIE CADDELL: Unipower
EDWARD FRANCIS: Vauxhall
Vignale
Volga
Volvo
MIKE KETTLEWELL: Unser
USAC
Villoresi
L. J. K. SETRIGHT: Two-Stroke Engine
Tyres
Tyrrell
Valve Gear
Valve Timing
Vanwall
ERWIN TRAGATSCH: Volkswagen
WORDSMITHS LTD: Universal Joint
Vacuum Gauge
Vibration

Picture acknowledgments
Page 2401: Bossaglia; Quattroruote; Quattroruote—**2402:** Quattroruote—**2403:** Quattroruote—**2404-5:** Bossaglia—**2406:** Quattroruote; Pirelli; Quattroruote—**2407:** Farabola; Michelin—**2408:** Quattroruote—**2409:** Pirelli; Firestone; Goodyear; Dunlop; Quattroruote; Michelin—**2410:** Alisi—**2410-11:** Papetti—**2411:** Alisi—**2412:** Papetti—**2413:** Papetti; Pellegrini—**2414:** Papetti—**2415:** Papetti—**2416:** Pirelli; Quattroruote; Quattroruote; Quattroruote—**2417:** I. Ward; F. Lini—**2418:** Papetti; D. Goodman—**2418-9:** Quattroruote—**2419:** I. Ward—**2420:** Quattroruote; M. Decet; L. J. Caddell—**2421:** National Motor Museum—**2422:** N. Bruce—**2422-3:** National Motor Museum—**2423:** National Motor Museum—**2424:** J. Spencer Smith—**2425:** J. Spencer Smith—**2426:** Autosport; J. Spencer Smith—**2427:** Fiat—**2428:** Di Santo—**2429:** Ceci—**2430:** Phipps Photographic; Indianapolis Motor Speedway—**2431:** Indianapolis Motor Speedway; Phipps Photographic—**2433:** London Art Tech—**2434:** IGDA; Phipps Photographic—**2434-5:** IGDA—**2436:** Orbis; Phipps Photographic—**2436-7:** London Art Tech—**2438:** Smith's Industries—**2439:** J. Spencer Smith—**2440:** National Motor Museum—**2441:** Fiat; Papetti—**2442:** Museo di Torino—**2444-5:** Quattroruote—**2448:** Papetti—**2450:** Nesta; Quattroruote—**2451:** Quattroruote; Papetti—**2452:** Nesta; Nesta; Nesta; Fiat; Fiat; Fiat—**2453:** British Leyland—**2454:** C. Burgess Wise—**2455:** British Leyland; British Leyland; National Motor Museum; National Motor Museum—**2456:** C. Pocklington; British Leyland—**2457:** British Leyland; National Motor Museum—**2458:** National Motor Museum—**2459:** National Motor Museum—**2460:** National Motor Museum; C. Posthumus—**2461:** J. Spencer Smith—**2462:** J. Spencer Smith—**2463:** National Motor Museum—**2464:** Quattroruote—**2465:** Di Santo; Vauxhall—**2466:** Vauxhall; Vauxhall; Vauxhall; National Motor Museum—**2467:** National Motor Museum; National Motor Museum; T. D. Houlding—**2468:** National Motor Museum—**2469:** National Motor Museum; Vauxhall; National Motor Museum—**2470:** Vauxhall—**2471:** National Motor Museum—**2472:** National Motor Museum; Vauxhall—**2473:** Vauxhall—**2474:** Vauxhall—**2475:** Vauxhall—**2476:** Vauxhall—**2477:** L. J. Caddell/Orbis—**2478:** Quattroruote—**2481:** Quattroruote; National Motor Museum; Veteran Car Club—**2482:** National Motor Museum; Veteran Car Club; National Motor Museum—**2483:** Quattroruote; National Motor Museum—**2484:** Ford; Quattroruote—**2485:** G. Gauld—**2486:** Dubbini—**2486-7:** G. Gauld—**2487:** Boschetti; Belli; Quattroruote—**2488-9:** Quattroruote—**2489:** Belli; Quattroruote—**2490:** M. Kettlewell—**2491:** National Motor Museum—**2492:** National Motor Museum—**2493:** Totnes Motor Museum—**2494:** Ceci; National Motor Museum; National Motor Museum—**2495:** Belli—**2496:** National Motor Museum (I)—**2497:** Moity; Quattroruote—**2498:** Archivio Anselmi; Bisconcini—**2499:** National Motor Museum—**2500:** Volga—**2501:** National Motor Museum—**2502:** National Motor Museum—**2503:** Volkswagen—**2504:** Volkswagen—**2505:** N. Bruce—**2506-7:** N. Bruce; Quattroruote—**2508:** L. J. Caddell/Orbis—**2509:** L. J. Caddell—**2510:** IMS—**2511:** National Motor Museum; Volvo—**2512-3:** Volvo—**2513:** National Motor Museum; Volvo—**2514:** Volvo—**2514-5:** G. Gauld—**2515:** National Motor Museum—**2516:** Volvo—**2517:** L. J. Caddell/Orbis—**2518:** National Motor Museum—**2519:** National Motor Museum—**2520:** C. Posthumus—**cover:** National Motor Museum; Volkswagen

Distributed by Columbia House, 51 West 52nd Street, New York, New York 10019
Printed in U.S.A.

Contents   Page

Section	Title	Page
AT WORK AND PLAY	Veteran & Vintage: Old, Older and Oldest	2481
CARS OF TODAY	Vauxhall Firenza	2476
	Vauxhall Chevette	2477
	Volkswagen Golf 1500LS	2508
	Volkswagen Scirocco	2509
	Volvo 245	2517
THE GREAT CARS	Unis: Consistent & Conservative	2421
	Unipower: Whatever Is It?	2424
	Vale: Hand-Made at Economy Price	2439
	Vauxhall	2465
	Vinot: The Cars That Ran "Silently"	2491
	Voisin: Spectacular and Efficient Cars From France	2493
	Volga: Part of Russia's Transportation System	2499
	Volkswagen: Dr. Ferdinand and the People's Car	2501
	Volvo: The Founder of Sweden's Motor Industry	2510
	Vulcan: Southport's God of Fire	2518
HOW IT WORKS	Two-Stroke Engine: Too Simple To Succeed	2401
	Tyres: Feat on the Ground	2406
	Universal Joint: Drive From Any Angle	2427
	Vacuum Gauge: Measuring Less Than Nothing	2438
	Valve Gear: Keeping the Gases in Check	2441
	Valve Timing: Choosing the Right Moment	2449
	Ventilation: Warm in Winter, Cool in Summer	2478
	Vibration: Shake, Rattle and Roll	2484
THE MOTOR INDUSTRY	Vanden Plas: Britain's Adopted Coachbuilder	2453
	Vignale: An Italian Styling Family	2485
WHO'S WHO	Unser: Pike's People	2430
	Varzi	2464
	Villoresi: The World Champion Teacher	2490
	Wagner: A Famous Driver From the Heroic Age	2520
WORLD OF SPEED	Tyrrell: A Shrewd Talent-Spotter	2417
	USAC: Discovering a New World	2433
	Vanderbilt Cup: The American Marathon	2458
	Vanwall: The End of An Era	2461
	Voiturette Racing: A Class Apart From the Grands Prix	2496

TOO SIMPLE TO SUCCEED

The two-stroke engine has never proved popular with large automobile companies because of its lack of efficiency

THE INVENTION OF SOMETHING NEW is all too easily corrupted by old ideas. Man was made in the image of God; the earliest aircraft were fashioned after the example of birds; and the two-stroke engine was strongly influenced by established steam practice. When the experimenters of the nineteenth century were engaged in the creation of the internal combustion engine, their thinking was pre-conditioned by familiarity with the already highly developed steam engine. It seemed natural and proper that every turn of the crankshaft (even of a single-cylinder engine, such as nearly all the pioneer types were) should produce power; in the course of one such revolution, the piston would make one stroke in each direction up and down its cylinder, and so the complete cycle would be completed in two strokes, during one of which the piston would be subjected to combustion pressure. The piston engine familiar in motor cars today is a four-

stroke: in other words, two rotations of the crankshaft (and correspondingly four alternating strokes of the piston) are necessary to the completion of one operating cycle. To engineers brought up on steam the idea seemed mildly preposterous: with so much of its working time apparently idle, and with such intermittent delivery of power, such an engine would surely be wasteful and irregular in its running. What was possibly even more cogent was the fact that the four-stroke cycle had been covered by patents taken out in 1876 by Otto and Langen.

Most of the pioneers of the two-stroke engine were working not with petrol but with Town's gas, and in some cases they actually contrived to emulate the steam engine even more faithfully with double-acting cylinders in which combustion pressure was applied to each side of the piston in turn. An example was the Lenoir engine (built on principles expounded by d'Humberstein in 1801), into which the mixture of gas and air was admitted to one or other end of the cylinder during an expansion phase, and then ignited immediately after closure of the slide valve at about half-stroke. It was, after all, a very slow-running engine, doing perhaps 50 rpm, and atmospheric pressure was

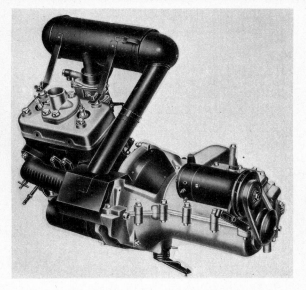

Above: the Saab 92 of 1949, the first production car to be produced by the Swedish company; its twin-cylinder two-stroke engine *(left)* had a capacity of 764 cc and was based on a design by the DKW concern

Far left: contrary to many opinions two-strokes are not invariably devoid of valves; in this design by Tony Huber for a Peugeot of 1906 an automatic poppet valve was placed in the inlet passage (this was closed by a weak spring and opened by suction); a sliding diaphragm was placed around the con-rod to seal the crankcase from the cylinder, thereby making the conveyance of the charge through the transfer port more efficient

enough to ensure reasonably good filling. No attempt was made to compress the charge, but the rapid expansion following its ignition was sufficient to propel the piston over the remaining half of its stroke, and at least the arrangement had the virtue of leaving the entire return stroke available for scavenging of the cylinder. So it was hopelessly inefficient from the thermal point of view, the absence of a compression phase limiting thermal efficiency to something like 4 per cent. Since even the early Otto or four-stroke engines contrived a thermal efficiency in the region of 25 per cent, it was clear that something was wrong; and those designers who were still wedded to the idea of one impulse per revolution reasoned that a separate charging pump was necessary to force the fresh mixture into the working cylinder. Once again they were thinking in steam terms, where the steam was delivered under high pressure into the cylinders; but it is important to recognize that what they were proposing was merely a charging pump, not a supercharging pump.

The first to do this effectively was Dugald Clerk, in 1881. He made use of a form of uniflow scavenge, the fresh charge entering the cylinder through a mechanically operated inlet valve in the cylinder head, while the vitiated gases made their exit through exhaust ports uncovered by the piston at the bottom of its stroke. A separate pumping cylinder forced the mixture in

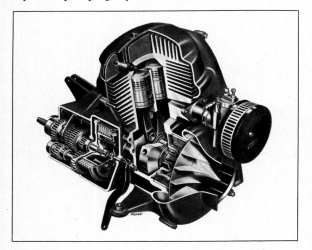

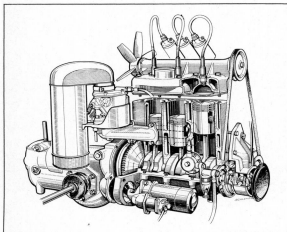

through the top valve, against the opposition of the rising piston, and the resulting compression raised thermal efficiency to about 15 per cent. Still it was a fairly clumsy arrangement, to be rapidly overtaken by the Day patent of 1889 for a two-stroke engine in which the crankcase was used as the pumping chamber, the gas being drawn into the crankcase through an automatic spring-loaded poppet valve, compressed in there by the descending piston, and transferred under that pressure through a passage leading to a port in the cylinder wall uncovered by the piston at the bottom of its stroke. Immediately opposite this port was another for the exhaust, a taller one which accordingly opened earlier and, rather awkwardly, therefore closed later. To prevent the incoming mixture flowing straight through and out the other side, a deflector on the piston crown diverted its path upwards towards the cylinder head, and by careful juggling of the relative openings and closures of the two ports, adequate scavenging and charging were achieved.

FIRST STROKE

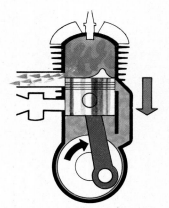

exhaust port — transfer port

inlet port

The exhaust port is open, inlet and transfer closed; the piston creates a crankcase depression

The piston starts compressing the charge; mixture enters the crankcase through the inlet port

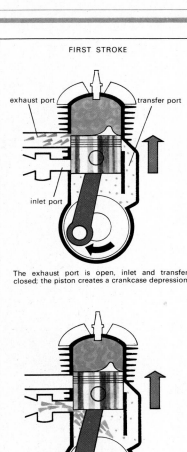

Compression finishes, combustion starts; mixture continues to enter through the inlet port

SECOND STROKE

Expansion has pushed the piston down the cylinder, opening the exhaust port and closing the inlet

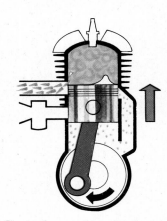

The transfer port opens and new mixture enters the cylinder, removing the remaining exhaust

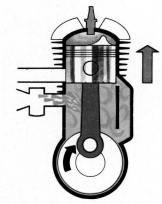

The transfer port closes, but the exhaust continues to leave; the cycle is then complete

Top left: an Isetta 236 cc, 10 bhp, compound-cylinder two-stroke of 1953, developed for motor-cycle use
Above left: the three-cylinder two-stroke engine used in the DKW 3–6 of 1949; its capacity was 896 cc and it had a power output of 36 bhp

This was the two-stroke engine that captured the popular imagination. It seemed to the layman that such an engine should be twice as powerful as a four-stroke of the same capacity, for did it not fill itself with fresh charge and burn it twice as often? Of course it did not: the filling was incomplete, the combustion likewise, its breathing condemned it to run slowly, and the efficiency could not bear comparison in thermal or volumetric terms with that of the four-stroke engine. On the other hand there was a blessed lack of mechanical complication, and in days when materials were poor and lubricants even worse, that was a very important consideration. It followed from the absence

Right: various types of
valve have been tried,
in order to control the
ingress to the crankcase
of fresh mixture more
effectively than by
using the more usual
method of the piston
covering and uncovering
the port

of complex mechanical valves that friction losses would
be much lower than in a four-stroke engine, although
the mechanical efficiency was somewhat reduced by the
losses involved in the pumping work being done in the
crankcase. All that remained was to get rid of the last
disposable moving part. The automatic inlet valve in
the crankcase gave way to an extra port in the cylinder
wall, communicating with the crankcase when the
piston approached the top of its stroke and its skirt
uncovered the port, through which fresh mixture would
rush in from the carburettor to fill the evacuated
crankcase. This at last was the mechanically minimal
engine that to many simple-minded early enthusiasts

combustion chamber, the piston crown, the ports, and
the sparking plug. Although the engine was mechanically quiet due to the absence of valve mechanism, its
exhaust was offensively noisy, because of the early and
necessarily sudden opening of the exhaust port to
ensure a quick discharge of the combustion gases before
the inlet port opened; but when silencers were added to
the exhaust pipe they quickly became clogged by
carbon too. What the engine gained in ease of maintenance it lost in the frequency with which it needed
attention.

Many ingenious attempts were made to overcome the
problem caused by the symmetrical openings of the

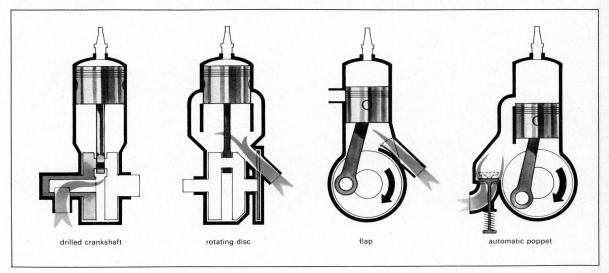

drilled crankshaft　　　　rotating disc　　　　flap　　　　automatic poppet

seemed to have everything in its favour.

Meanwhile, Otto and Langen, working in the Deutz
firm with the assistance of the accomplished Wilhelm
Maybach, had been getting very good results with their
four-stroke engines; and when in 1890 it became
apparent that their patents were at least questionable
and at best unenforceable, everybody started to copy
them—not least Karl Benz, who had patented his own
quite clever and efficient two-stroke engines in about
1882, but was eager to make the change. Thereafter the
simple Day-cycle 2-stroke engine was condemned for
decades to serve only the humblest of purposes in
motorcycles and light cars.

Quite simply, the two-stroke engine had proved a
considerable disappointment. It behaved erratically,
running cleanly and sweetly at some speeds and yet
behaving in a most peculiar fashion at others, perhaps
firing only at every fourth or eighth stroke. Engineers of
the time simply did not understand the gas dynamics,
the pulsating air flows, the resonances of inlet and
exhaust systems, which are so crucial a part in the
charging and scavenging processes of the two-stroke
engine. Moreover there were severe practical
difficulties: the introduction of the petrol and air
mixture to the crankcase subjected the bearings there to
a constant wash of petrol that tended to scour away any
lubricating oil, and yet pressure-fed plain bearings
could not be used, because the flow of oil from them
would be so copious as to ruin the mixture transferred
to the cylinder. Instead, a proportion of oil had to be
mixed with the petrol, enough to lubricate the roller
bearings of the crankshaft, and yet not so much as to
contaminate the mixture to the point where combustion
was imperilled. The outcome was unpleasantly smelly
and smoky, while such burnt oil as did not emerge from
the exhaust pipe in a rich blue haze was deposited as a
liberal coating of carbon on the surfaces of the

inlet and exhaust ports. If only the inlet could be
arranged to close after the exhaust, as well as opening
after, things would be a lot better. This was contrived in
the 'split single' engine, in which two parallel cylinders
shared a common combustion chamber, while their
pistons were linked to the same crankpin. Both cylinders being effectively offset with their motions were out
of phase, and if one cylinder were furnished only with
an inlet port, and the other only with an exhaust port of
the same depth, the desired asymmetry of port timing
could be achieved. This principle was applied with
some success to motorcycle engines, surviving well into
the 1950s, but its only notable use in cars was in the
engine of the old Trojan of the twenties and thirties.
This was a peculiarly barbaric design: whereas the
geometrical complexities of the system were recognized
in other split singles by articulation of one of the
connecting rods, the Trojan was somehow made to
work with a simple V-shaped connecting rod clamped
at its apex around the big end. With such an arrangement the pistons ought to jam in their bores, but in fact
the conrods flexed! It was hardly surprising that the
Trojan engine could not run at high speeds nor deliver
high power, but the validity of the basic principle was
demonstrated by its extraordinary pulling power at very
low speeds: there have been few cars more adept at
climbing hills, and a Trojan was still competing
successfully in trials in the late 1950s, keeping everybody waiting for ages as it crawled up the most
forbidding acclivities, but never coming to a halt, even
on bad surfaces.

Other methods of securing asymmetric timing were
also tried. One was to have two opposing pistons in a
single cylinder, each linked to a crankshaft that was
slightly out of phase with the other, and each controlling at the outward extremity of its stroke a set of ports in
the cylinder wall. One piston uncovered inlet ports, the

Right: in order to make it possible to arrange for the inlet port to open and close after the exhaust, a novel twin-cylinder system was tried by several manufacturers; the cylinders shared a common combustion chamber and this layout was a great help in promoting efficient exhaust scavenging; the Isetta design was used in the engine shown on page 2404

Below right: two-stroke engines are generally characterised by uncomplicated construction and by a small number of cylinders however, this DRB engine was an exception because, produced as a prototype in 1967, it had six horizontally opposed cylinders with a capacity of 1000 cc, three rotary valves and three carburettors; it produced 115 bhp at 9000 rpm

other exhaust ports, and with unidirectional gas flow through the cylinder, high performance seemed guaranteed by the good scavenging promised. This configuration had been pioneered in the Ochelhauser gas engine in the nineteenth century, and was explored by Fiat in experiments with a 1½ litre supercharged Grand Prix engine intended for the races of 1927. Even today, when a number of high-speed diesels successfully exploit the obvious advantages of this layout, they do so only after painstaking attention to lubrication and cooling of the piston which controls the exhaust port. In the 1920s, there were neither the oils nor the metals, nor even the sparking plugs, necessary to sustain the high temperatures and severe heat gradients concentrated around the exhaust ports and the crown of the exhaust piston; and although the engine could be made to produce a power output almost as beyond belief as its noise output, Fiat soon recognized that it was not a practical proposition: the engine was never raced, its place being taken by a brilliant 12-cylinder four-stroke that was in the event even more powerful, utterly reliable, and completely successful.

One of the virtues of the opposed-piston two-stroke is that its pistons can be symmetrical, needing no deflectors on their crowns. The piston-top deflector is a nuisance because it adds extra weight, because it causes asymmetric expansion and therefore distortion of the piston as it grows hot, because it presents corners and edges that are susceptible to overheating and can in turn cause pre-ignition and detonation, and because it interfers with the design of a good combustion chamber shape. The elimination of the deflector by the invention of loop scavenging by Schneurle in Germany in the 1920s allowed considerable advances to be made in two-stroke engine development. The principle was to exploit the kinetic energy of the new charge entering through the transfer ports, these ports and their associated passages being so shaped that the streams of mixture emerging from them converged in the centre of the cylinder and travelled upwards towards the head, displacing the burnt charge which travelled in the opposite direction towards the exhaust port. At least two transfer ports were needed, diametrically opposed and angled away from the exhaust port; and when after some experimentation the correct layout was found, it became possible to exploit the improved piston shape and cooling to permit very high compression ratios to be used in conjunction with the best possible crankcase breathing that could be devised, and suddenly the two-stroke engine was a lot better than it ever had been. The system was earnestly developed by DKW in Germany, first in their motorcycles, and then in some car engines that were destined to survive under other names for generations to come.

The basic DKW car engine was an in-line three-cylinder water-cooled one, using Schneurle's loop scavenging. As usual in multi-cylinder two-strokes, the crankcase was internally divided: there must be a separate pumping chamber for each cylinder, one of the design problems being to minimise the volume of this chamber as much as possible in order to secure high compression ratio in it. Early versions relied on the traditional petroil lubrication, in which oil is mixed with the petrol in the tank, a practice that has given the oil companies some headaches, though they can now produce oils that remain in suspension in the petrol instead of settling to the bottom of the tank In later versions a positive pumped lubrication system was devised in which oil delivery was arranged from a separate tank in proportion to engine speed, and also to engine load.

In sizes up to about 850cc this three-cylinder engine

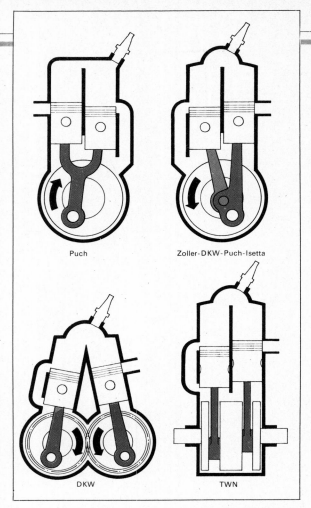

Puch   Zoller-DKW-Puch-Isetta

DKW   TWN

was quite satisfactory, having the virtues of compact overall dimensions, excellent balance, very smooth torque delivery and quite good performance, at some cost in fuel consumption. The engine employed by Saab when they began car manufacture after the war was essentially similar, and sporting versions were developed to give quite high performance, though not without some show of temperament. To make the engine more powerful without loss of tractability, it would have been preferable to make it bigger; but it had already been long established that the two-stroke petrol engine runs into severe difficulties of scavenging and cooling if the individual cylinders are bigger than about 300 cc, and although DKW eventually made a three-cylinder engine of 1175 cc displacement, it was clear that they were going down a dead end. In the 1960s, as the popular demand for more performance caused car manufacturers to make their engines more powerful and usually bigger, the simple little two-stroke engine was generally abandoned. It is difficult to make a big one with a multiplicity of cylinders, very difficult to make a good one with large cylinders—and practically impossible to make one with a clean exhaust, so the increasing stringency of legislation against atmospheric pollution has virtually killed the two-stroke as a car engine. It still survives in Europe in the East German Wartburg, which is the old DKW all over again.

Although we are not strictly concerned with them here, large diesel engines and small motorcycle engines continue to exploit two-stroke principles, sometimes to considerable advantage, and all the really worthwhile developments of the type have been made in these fields. On the diesel side we can see pressure scavenging (sometimes aided by turbocharging), asymmetrical timing with uniflow scavenging either by means of opposed pistons or by combining piston-controlled inlet ports with mechanically valved exhaust ports, and numerous other refinements that are all made possible by the fact that the diesel engine ingests only air, its fuel being added by direct injection into the combustion space when all the ports are well and truly closed. In the motorcycle engines, we may trace the history of tuning for extravagent power at enormous cost in fuel consumption and loss of flexibility: control of induction timing into the crankcase through a large diameter disc valve attached to the crankshaft was a feature of such engines for many years, the valve having been invented by one Zimmerman and the resultant engine being very highly developed by the brilliant Walter Kaaden of MZ in East Germany. After pursuing the same course for some time, the leading Japanese protagonists Yamaha and Suzuki reverted to piston-controlled porting with complicated transfer passages, but with further work on resonant exhaust systems (based on divergent-convergent nozzle theories) and more recently of reed valves in the induction system to inhibit flow reversal, small racing two-strokes now develop extraordinarily high specific powers, with noise levels to match. Similar principles are applied to small outboard marine engines, but as far as the motor car is concerned the two-stroke is virtually dead. Outside the isolated pockets of East Europe and Japan there was until recently one source of hope for the engine's future: Audi–VW were experimenting with a direct-injection uniflow petrol engine for use in cars, achieving good fuel economy and control of emissions as long ago as 1973; but latest intelligence suggests that the project has been dropped.   LJKS

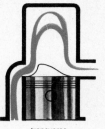

transverse

unidirectional

tangential

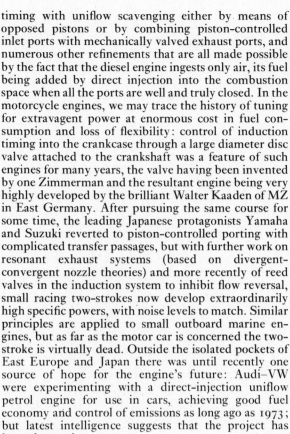

opposing currents

tangential with 3 currents

Above: the position of the ports governs the gas flow in a two-stroke, this diagram shows the types of layout in use

Left: a Junkers diesel two-stroke, in which two pistons of unequal stroke move in one cylinder; pure air, rather than mixture is drawn in, so on unburnt fuel is lost down the exhaust pipe

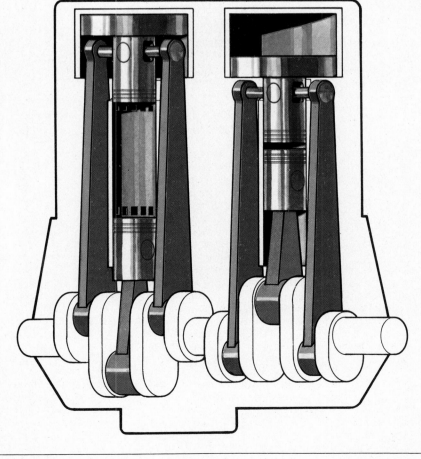

FEAT ON THE GROUND

The many and amazing properties of the modern tyre combine to make motoring safe and comfortable

Publicity material from the early years of Pirelli, one of the oldest tyre companies, established in 1872; the periods are the turn of the century, *bottom far right*, the 1910s, *top far right*, and the 1930s, *near right*

THE MEN WHO MOCKED John Boyd Dunlop's pneumatic tyre did so because it was perfectly clear to them that a rubber tube filled with air, even at a considerable pressure, would not be amenable to the least rigorous of disciplines, and that any vehicle riding on such a device would soon display an alarming lack of controllability. What they failed to appreciate was the part played by the fabric which was a vital component of the primordial pneumatic tyre. Even today it is common for laymen to say that the air is carrying the load—and in laymen's language there is an element of truth in this.

There are currently two basic types of carcass construction: one is commonly known as radial-ply, the other as cross-ply—although bias-ply or diagonal-ply would be more accurate descriptions of the latter. Combinations of the two types are also possible and have been tried from time to time.

The bias-ply is the oldest established version. In this the carcass consists of two or more layers of virtually unwoven fabric—i.e. all warp and no weft. The cords or threads in these layers run at an angle from one rim bead to the other. Each bead consists of a fairly stiff hoop of strong wire embedded in rubber which serves to prevent the tyre from stretching and so leaving the wheel rim, and also as an anchorage for the layers of carcass cords. This anchorage may be reinforced by additional layers of cord in more or less narrow strips

wrapped around the bead and extending for a short distance up the lower sidewall to help in bearing the severe stresses to which this clinch area around the bead is subjected. There are several variations in the arrangement of these bead wrappers, but our primary concern must be with the basic and indispensable layers or plies of carcass cords.

These layers are superimposed so that their diagonal cords lie in opposite directions, crossing to form a biased or latticed pattern. Actual inter-weaving of the cords, as in woven fabric, cannot be permitted because of the considerable friction that would occur between the cords as the carcass is flexed.

Because the pneumatic tyre must not only cushion the ride of the vehicle, but also provides its means of direction, some sort of compromise must be reached in establishing the angle at which the cords run across the tread from bead to bead. This is because the requirements of comfort and directional stability are mutually opposed. When the cords are at an angle approaching the circumferential direction of the tread, the tyre will give good stability and steering response but a harsh ride, and as speed and inflation pressure increase, the cross-sectional shape of the tyre will show considerable distortion. If on the other hand the cords could be turned until they were at right angles to the tread circumference, the ride would be the softest obtainable but the lateral stability of the tyre would disappear almost completely. For many years the obvious compromise was adopted where the cords ran at an angle of 45 degrees across the tyre, the angle between the cord

Below left: the main problem with pneumatic tyres has always been the possibility of a blow-out; this 1906 picture shows the difficulty of repairing such a puncture in the early days of motoring

Below: a Michelin 'town and country' type of tyre

explained, such a construction gives great pliability but little or no directional or dimensional stability, and this defect is rectified by the interior belt of cords running circumferentially around the carcass.

The belt has not only to prevent the radial growth of the tyre but also to provide directional stability and steering response. This is possible because, although flexible in one plane, it resists deformation in the other, behaving like a slender beam or girder. To assist in maintaining this lateral stiffness the belt is made of at least two layers of cords, which are not quite truly circumferential, but slightly diagonal, the angles usually being in the region of 18 to 22 degrees. The number of layers varies according to the material of which the cords are made and the amount of lateral stiffness desired. When the cords are spun from fine steel wire there are almost invariably (in car tyres) only two layers or plies of breaker cords; when the cords are made of rayon or polyester, the number of plies may be four, five or even six. It is very rare to find seven.

Until World War II practically all tyres had carcasses

and the equatorial or centre line of the tread being known as the crown angle. Later this angle was reduced to about 40 degrees, and 30 degrees or even less for tyres built for very high speeds.

The idea behind the radial-ply tyre was to eliminate this compromise in cord angles and to divide the carcass into two parts, one to provide the desired ride qualities and the other the necessary directional qualities. By motoring standards the idea is of great antiquity. It can be traced back to a British patent granted prior to World War I to Messrs Gray and Sloper. Their claim was sufficiently detailed in 1913 to establish all the basic principles of the radial-ply tyre from which all subsequent patterns have evolved.

In 1913 it was thought that the girder belt should be on the inside of the casing, beneath the tyre tread; but today the manufacturers of radial-ply tyres universally put the belt on the outside of the casing. This belt consists of a relatively stiff band of cords that have adequate flexibility but great resistance to stretching: being inextensible, they are relied upon entirely to restrict the radial growth of the inflated tube. Paradoxically, this inability of the belted tyre's circumference to expand serves to prevent it from contracting in the same way as does the part of a cross-ply tyre's circumference in the region of the contact area, but this is something into which we will go later. At any rate the inextensible nature of this broad belt makes it behave like a girder in its own plane, preventing it from distorting or flexing appreciably in any plane but that at right-angles to its surface.

This being so, it is possible to introduce the other essential feature of the construction, tyre cords running radially from bead to bead—that is, crossing the crown of the tyre at right angles, not diagonally. As already

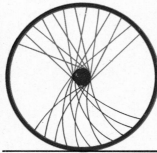

Left: the pneumatic tyre functions in much the same way as the spoked wheel; the mass of the car is born on the cords at the top of the tyre and not on the air which serves only to soften the ride and keep the cords taut

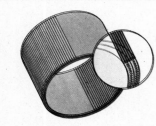
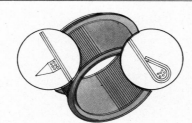

a cylinder of rubberised with large axial strands in two layers

application and fixing of the rubber and metal beading

shaping of the carcass and application of the cord belt

application and rolling of the tread material

Above: this publicity poster of 1898 introduced the 'Michelin Man', Mr Bibendum, for the first time

Left: diagrammatic representations of the various stages in tyre manufacture

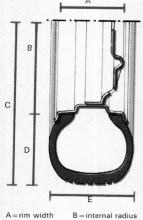

A = rim width   B = internal radius

C = external radius   D = height

E = width

Above: the dimensions of a tyre

Above and right: three pictures showing the manufacturing process of early pneumatic tyres; the fabric carcass is being fitted to a former in the first photograph and the bead applied in the second; in the third picture, *right*, the rubber has been applied and vulcanised and the tyre is being taken out of its mould

Left: just a few of the many tyre-company emblems

Below: graphical representations of tyre-function variations

Bottom: the Michelin XAS asymmetric-tread radial tyre

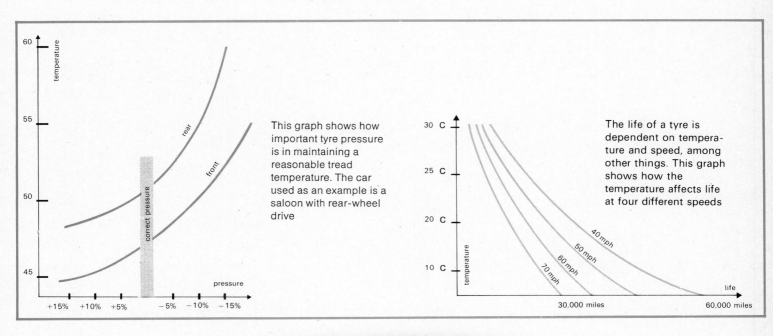

This graph shows how important tyre pressure is in maintaining a reasonable tread temperature. The car used as an example is a saloon with rear-wheel drive

The life of a tyre is dependent on temperature and speed, among other things. This graph shows how the temperature affects life at four different speeds

Right: a selection of automobile tyres chosen from various motoring periods—from left to right and top to bottom they are Pirelli Cord (1900–10), Dunlop (1900–10), Michelin (1910), Martin (1910), Goodrich Ballon (1915), Goodrich Souple Cord (1918–25), Pirelli Super Flex (1918–25), Dunlop (1920), Dunlop (1930), Michelin (1930), Pirelli White Star (1935) and Metzeler asymmetrical (1952–3)

made of long staple cotton; but then rayon was introduced, not as a means of making a stronger carcass but as a means of saving rubber. A rayon tyre could be made thinner than a cotton one of equivalent strength, and therefore needed less rubber to separate the plies and cords from each other to prevent chafing. Cotton rapidly disappeared, and rayon is the staple material in the majority of tyres today.

More recently nylon was introduced, originally in aircraft tyres. It is stronger, more elastic, more flexible and consequently cooler running than rayon, and is therefore used principally in tyres built for high speeds or heavy loads. Its elasticity makes it unsuitable for use in radial-ply tyres on its own, although it is sometimes used in ultra-high-speed radial-ply tyres in combination with other materials. Even in bias-ply tyre, however, it has certain disadvantages, the most evident being a tendency towards what is called flat spotting or cold flatting: the nylon cords tend to lose their flexibility when cold, and if a tyre is left to stand for

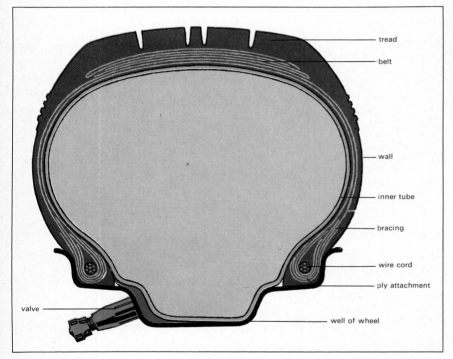

Above: a section through a tubed radial tyre

Far right: as cars have become faster, so tyre design has had to change; not only have materials improved, but the shape of the tyre has altered considerably

some time, the deformation of the carcass where the tyre is resting on the road takes on a semi-permanent nature, so that when the car is driven again the ride is harsh and bumpy until the tyre casing has warmed up sufficiently to recover its flexibility.

For many years, efforts have been made to substitute Terylene (or polyester) as a carcass material, the principal difficulty having been the achieving of a satisfactory bond between this and the rubber. The material is tough and durable, but its principal attraction to the tyre manufacturer is a lower cost of production.

We may note briefly the recent development of glass fibre as a material for the cords of rigid breakers. Glass is exceptionally strong and surprisingly elastic, but special techniques have to be used to prevent chafing of the glass filaments that must be wound or spun into cords, and further expertise is necessary to achieve a satisfactory bonding of the glass to the rubber. Subject to the few exceptions already noted, the breaker plies of radial-ply tyres are made exclusively of steel or rayon; and although the trend of the 1960s was towards a more general adoption of rayon, there are now signs of a

reversal of this trend. Recently, manufacturers have increasingly returned to the use of steel.

This reversal is due to the important part played by breaker construction in determining the tread-wear resistance of the radial-ply tyre. The resistance of the breaker band to edgewise bending is responsible for the dimensional stability of the tread in the contact patch; and in fact the greatest possible rigidity is achieved by the use of steel breaker cords at a low crown angle.

The greater beam stiffness of the steel belt is not the only attraction of steel; its greater strength allows the use of fewer plies and thus encourages a thinning of the tyre. The situation is analogous to the reasons for replacing cotton with rayon in bias-ply tyres: less rubber is required, and therefore the tyre can flex more easily, the build-up of heat is less rapid, and the dissipation of the heat accumulated occurs more readily due to the reduced ratio of mass to surface area.

Rayon is preferred in the carcass because it forms an exceptionally strong bond with the rubber to which it is

permits lateral displacement of the tread with respect to its relationship with the rim.

Thus these differences in basic construction give the radial-ply tyre lower rolling resistance than the bias-ply alternative, longer tread life, higher cornering power at smaller slip angles, better tractive and braking grip, a better high-speed ride, and comparative freedom from centrifugal growth, from wander induced by longitudinal ridges in the road surface, and from side loadings induced by wheel camber. Together with these advantages, there are disadvantages: a harsher low-speed ride, heavier steering at low speeds and when parking, a tendency to break away more suddenly at the ultimate limit of adhesion, an occasional instability in S-bends, and a certain vulnerability of the sidewalls.

Rubber is a marvellous material, but a weird one. It is very non-linear in its behaviour, which offends engineers; but it is also remarkably accommodating, which delights them.

Vulcanization makes the natural *plastic* material (that

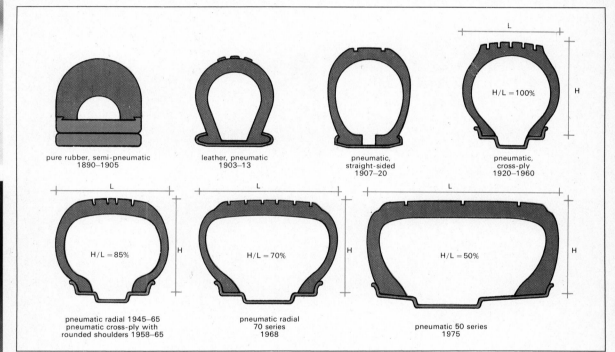

pure rubber, semi-pneumatic
1890–1905

leather, pneumatic
1903–13

pneumatic,
straight-sided
1907–20

pneumatic,
cross-ply
1920–1960
$H/L = 100\%$

pneumatic radial 1945–65
pneumatic cross-ply with
rounded shoulders 1958–65
$H/L = 85\%$

pneumatic radial
70 series
1968
$H/L = 70\%$

pneumatic 50 series
1975
$H/L = 50\%$

mated, and because satisfactory flexibility is combined with a good resistance to endwise stretch.

This whole problem of sidewall stiffness has been the subject of concentrated study in the past few years, in the effort to improve the handling characteristics of radial-ply tyres in the more violent type of manoeuvres. It was some time before designers learned the importance of controlling the flexibility of the sidewalls in radial-ply tyres, as this flexibility permits an appreciable delay in response between tyre tread and wheel rim. Furthermore, radial-ply sidewalls are especially sensitive to the transmission of tractive or braking torques which (according to circumstances) may degrade or heighten their lateral response.

Work on this problem has led to the evolution of what might be called the 'second generation' of radial-ply tyres, in which the real or apparent stiffness of the sidewalls has been increased in order to improve lateral response. This capacity for lateral distortion is called side-wall compliance. The flexural ability of the sidewalls should not be reduced, as this accommodates variations in the distance between the tread and the wheel rim; but it is advisable to avoid the distortion that

is, one which flows under the effect of heat or pressure) into an *elastic* one which, after stretching, returns to its original shape. This is the critical property in engineering, the key to the term 'elastomer' that we use to describe all materials, natural or otherwise, that have this particular rubbery property.

A further property of elastomers is unique: when stretched they become warm, and when contracted they become cool. Conversely they can display what is known as the Joule effect, contracting when heated and elongating when cool. Today there are fifteen families of elastomers many of them suitable for incorporation in tyre compounds.

Now that such a large variety of polymers and compounding ingredients for tyre rubber is available, the tyre designer has much more scope in the selection of a compound for a particular job. Tyres perform in a great variety of conditions, each one calling for a tread compound or a combination of compounds in the tyre, each with its own particular behaviour and characteristics. As in most kinds of design, success depends on achieving the best possible compromise, and one physical property in rubber is often obtainable only at the expense of others that are equally desirable.

To appreciate what the tyre chemist has to face, let us briefly consider the various enemies of rubber in one form or another. Probably the greatest of these enemies is heat which, if allowed to build up unchecked, will eventually cause chemical and physical degradation of the vulcanized rubber and a disastrous loss of strength. The heat may be put into a tyre by radiation or conduction from its surroundings, but most of it is the product of internal friction resulting from the inevitable flexure of the tyre as it rolls along the road. The tyre being an elastic body, its entire structure is subject to one flexure in the course of one complete rotation of the tyre. Fifteen years ago an average car tyre would suffer 750 flexures in the course of a mile, suffering them at the rate of about 20 flexures per second when the car was doing 100 mph. The corresponding figure today is more likely to approach 980 flexures per mile or 27 flexures per second at 100 mph. Every flexure involves a displacement of material and therefore the generation of internal friction in the tyre material, which inevitably engenders heat. Furthermore, friction heat attributable to the transmission of tractive, cornering or braking efforts on the road surface, and any of the other things that may cause abrasion or distortion, must be considered.

Rubbers are also generally susceptible to chemical attack, being unsaturated organic compounds which

wet cobblestones, but if it excels in any one of these things it will probably have little capacity to deal with the others.

The term *hysteresis* should be explained before proceeding further. 'High hysteresis' is a comparative term, and for the sake of definition it is applied to compounds having a rebound resilience of appreciably

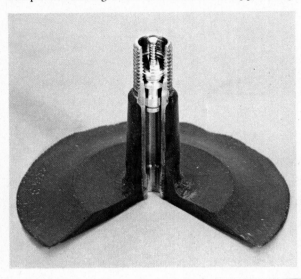

Left: a cutaway view of a tubeless-tyre valve; the rubber base is vulcanised into the tyre carcass and the valve core is screwed into the housing

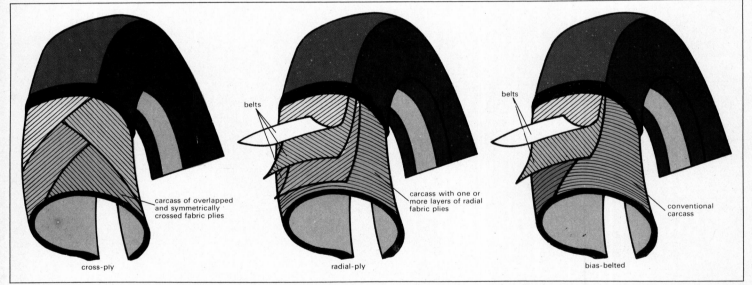

carcass of overlapped and symmetrically crossed fabric plies

cross-ply

belts

carcass with one or more layers of radial fabric plies

radial-ply

belts

conventional carcass

bias-belted

often react with other chemical reagents. Acids, chlorine, hydrogen, sulphur, oxides of nitrogen, and many other everyday commodities may be severely degrading. Even atmospheric oxygen attacks rubber, slowly causing it to become hard and brittle. Ozone attacks it more rapidly and is often present in greater concentrations than might be thought. Many liquids act as solvents of rubber; water, alcohol and acetone do not but petrol, benzine, turpentine, carbon tetrachloride and several other things will cause rubber to swell and disperse. This is a convenient way of making viscous cements, but very damaging to tyres. Even ultra-violet light can damage rubber.

There are other problems that must be dealt with by the tread rubber. Abrasion resistance is an obvious one, as are resistance to tearing and cutting (which are not related). Furthermore the tread must be compounded so as to behave in the desired way on wet roads, cold roads, hot roads or even where there are no roads at all. It may be expected to grip best on snow, melting ice, or

less than 50 per cent at a temperature of 50 degrees centigrade. In other words, it only gives back half the energy that is put into deforming it. The other half is absorbed, which is what hysteresis means. A high-hysteresis rubber is less springy, less resilient, than a natural rubber: it does not have the characteristic lively rebound, but is sluggish. Because of this it has a greater tendency to stay in intimate contact with the road surface, to envelop any projections of surface texture, and thus to provide very good grip, especially when the surface is wet. This last feature is quite remarkable, for water is a natural lubricant not only of natural rubber but also of many synthetic varieties; this will be discussed later. However, there is relatively high internal friction in such a rubber, and an obvious corollary of this is a considerable power absorption, therefore a car fitted with tyres of extra-high-grip rubber may be slightly slower and have a slightly heavier fuel consumption than one running on tyres of more resilient rubber.

Above: the three types of tyre reinforcement in common use in the 1970s; the bias belted tyre is a combination of cross-ply and radial-ply constructions

The perplexing situation is made yet more confusing by the effect of temperature on the performance of these various types of rubbers. For any particular one, the coefficient of friction that it can manifest on a given road surface rises to a peak as its temperature is increased to a certain point, and then as the temperature rises further the coefficient of friction becomes reduced.

violent acceleration and braking increase the tyre temperature markedly. Further one must remember that the essence of the high hysteresis, lazy, or 'cling' rubber is a high level of internal friction which tends to make the tyre run hot, in contrast to the cooler and more friction-free tyre treaded with highly resilient or low-hysteresis polymers.

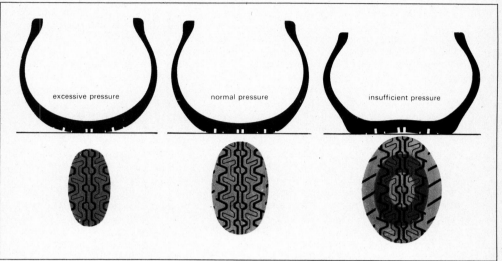

excessive pressure   normal pressure   insufficient pressure

Above left: the Pirelli BS3 tyre, characterised by its interchangeable tread bands

Above: diagrams showing how tyre-pressure settings affect the amount of tread which rests on the road

Left: radial covers are used in racing as well as on the road; these are tyres which were available for use at Mugello in 1975 by the victorious Alpine team

An important thing to bear in mind here is that the critical temperature is that of the rubber, not that of the road nor that of the surrounding air. Climate certainly makes a difference, but not as much as the duties to which the tyre is subjected. The bigger the tyre's load-bearing capacity, the higher its inflation pressure, or the greater its diameter, the cooler it will run; and of course the additional frictional heat built up by the trellising motion of the carcass cords in a bias-ply tyre is absent from the radial-ply tyre, which therefore runs cooler still. The high-speed tyre (deliberately designed with relatively thin treads and shallow shoulders to avoid heat build-up) can dissipate its heat more readily than tyres of more conventional proportions, profiting more from air cooling amongst other things. On the other hand high speeds, heavy loads, rough road surfaces,

Several practical conclusions can be drawn from this. First, it is not strictly possible to state flatly that a particular tyre provides particularly good grip either on the roads in general, or on wet or snowy roads in particular: judgement must be related to the temperature. This has been a particular problem in racing: tread compounds for Formula One Grand Prix tyres are often designed to function at temperatures exceeding 100 degrees C, but if the track be wet they may not even reach 100 degrees F. The problems of producing a satisfactory all-weather racing tyre are therefore enormous. Even for ordinary road-going vehicles the all-weather tyre is little more than an illusion.

The detailed differences in carcass construction are usually concealed within the tyre. The secrets locked within the rubber are for all practical purposes unfathomable. Unlike these, the tread pattern is there to be seen and judged. There are (for once) some sound and simple criteria to support one's judgement, making it possible to evaluate by eye the tyre's probable behaviour in terms of noise, grip, and wear.

Noise may be generated by a tyre in three different ways. First there is the squeal that is caused by friction between rubber and road surface and varies according to the nature of the rubber compound. There are also various types of vibration caused either by the roughness of the road surface or by the distortion of the tyre carcass as it revolves. Noise is also generated by the tread pattern itself. This is overcome by introducing deliberate irregularities into the tyre pattern, slightly varying the size of tread blocks or the zig-zag pattern of grooves so as to dampen the sound rather than to amplify it.

The matter of grip is more complicated. On a clean dry road surface the maximum grip is given by a completely smooth tyre, since this will put the greatest possible area of rubber in contact with the road. But the slightest presence of moisture on the road transforms it into something lethally dangerous.

It must be recognised that the retention of tyre grip on the road is a matter which is dependent as much on the nature of the tread pattern as on the chemistry of the tread compound. Where the road surface is smooth, the nature of the rubber is far less important than the ability of the tread pattern to push the surface water out of the way so that the tyre rubber can at least grip the road metal in some places. Where the road surface is open-textured and thus to some extent self-draining, the tread pattern cannot and need not function so effectively in sweeping aside water; the important factor is the degree of friction that can be realized between the rubber and the road where they make contact at the pinnicle of every irregularity. It is a useless over-simplification to talk about a given tyre being good or bad in the wet.

The tread pattern has two basic functions: it must provide drainage and bite. These two ideals are to some extent conflicting. Bite is the easier function to understand: the tread needs a quantity of reasonably sharp

well-defined edges that will engage with the road surface to provide some mechanical rather than merely frictional transmission of load; these edges need to be transverse for good traction and braking and longitudinal for steering and cornering. Most car manoeuvres involve both, and their needs can be met by resolving these forces into diagonal biting edges in the tread pattern.

However, the tyre may never come sufficiently close to the road surface for these edges to engage with it, if there is much water on the road. On streaming wet surfaces the water may build up in front of the tyre as a wedge, which at speed will be driven underneath to raise the tyre clear of the road and make it completely waterborne. This is termed aquaplaning.

If water is not to build up ahead of the tyre on a wet road, it must either be swept aside or be channelled away. Sweeping aside is clearly difficult at high speeds, especially with the wider tyres that are gradually and on the whole sensibly becoming fashionable. The same trend makes nonsense of some manufacturers' theories about lateral drainage of water through tread channels leading to the shoulders: this works well for the outermost portions of the tread, but satisfactory drainage of the middle portion can only be achieved by the provision of longitudinal passages. For effective drainage these must be as straight as possible and unimpeded. The removal of obstructions is comparatively easy in the case of a radial-ply tyre, whose tread is relatively free from distortion so that its grooves need not be closed by buttresses put there to support the ribs. Ensuring that the groove is absolutely straight, however, removes the necessary transverse biting elements from the tread pattern and so lessens performance in acceleration and braking.

When a car stands on its tyres they will, whatever their kind, suffer a certain amount of deflection and distortion. When the car moves, further distortions are superimposed on this basic one.

The effectiveness with which a tyre transmits tractive, braking or cornering forces to the road surface is affected by the variations in size and loading of the contact area. Because the contact area or 'footprint' of a radial-ply tyre is greater than that of an equivalent bias-ply tyre performing the same duties, such a tyre gives a better flotation effect. Its action is analogous to that of a track laid by a crawler vehicle: the ground pressure is relatively low and very evenly distributed. The same applies to any tyre that is run at a relatively low inflation

Below: the construction of a radial tyre. The synthetic rubber is mixed with lamp black and squeezed into a continuous strip (1), while the fabric weave is impregnated with rubber and cut into strips (2). This fabric is rolled onto a drum to form a cylinder and narrow strips are added each side to form the sidewalls (3). The cylinder is transferred to another machine where it is inflated and squeezed into shape (4); at this stage the bracing belts are added (5). The tread bands are next glued, cut and applied to the belts (6). The final process is to vulcanise the tyre to make the parts stick together and to give them elasticity; it is heated and squeezed in a press, which also adds the tread pattern and the writing (7 & 8)

pressure, and the effect is to give better grip on mud, sand and other loose surfaces.

On the other hand there are occasions when penetration rather than flotation is required. The small-section high-pressure tyre can often produce better results in snow (which has no shear strength) or on very thin ice (on frosted roads for example) than the large low-pressure tyre.

It must be remembered that load transfer during

Below: four pieces of tyre from various eras; *top left,* 1906, *top right,* 1917, *bottom left,* 1927, *bottom right,* 1947

braking, acceleration, cornering, or combinations of braking or acceleration with cornering, will similarly vary the size of the contact patch.

The reason for the change for tyre and pressures having dropped considerably, especially markedly in the last ten years, is simply that lower profiles offer the possibilities of improvement in most performance parameters except ride comfort, which is sensibly decreased. All these changes, whether improvements or otherwise, are derived from the generally greater vertical and lateral stiffness of the low profile tyre. There must be accepted as its characteristics, although it is perfectly possible to build a low-profile tyre that is less stiff in both directions than a given tyre of higher profile.

The greater vertical stiffness is responsible for the less comfortable ride of such a tyre and for its greater load-carrying capacity. A more important effect of the increased vertical stiffness is the change it makes in the shape of the contact patch, which becomes shorter and wider. Many performance parameters are changed by this simple readjustment of proportions. It will run cooler and last longer and may even demand a different type of rubber compound in order to suit these different temperatures or to exploit the better wear potential. Finally there are the changes in tyre behaviour brought about by the increased lateral stiffness of a low profile, these involving increased sensitivity to camber variations and a more prompt response to steering inputs.

There are greater complications issuing from the interdependence of load, inflation pressure and cornering power. The cornering force that the tyre is capable of sustaining may increase up to a certain point with an increase in the load that it is carrying, and beyond that point it will decrease again. If, instead of altering the load, the inflation pressure is altered, the same thing may or may not happen: up to a certain point the cornering ability increases, but beyond that point it may or may not increase, again according to the type and size of the tyre and the load it is carrying. Thus armed with one or two basic principles it can be seen that there are circumstances in which the car on fat tyres may in fact corner no faster than a car on thin tyres, although it generally has better handling characteristics.

An increase in rim width may have the effect of reducing sidewall compliance in even the most flexible of conventional radial-ply tyres. Within reasonable limits the idea is a good one, but the limits beyond which it becomes dangerous are strict: the mode of flexure may be very different from what the sidewalls were originally intended to suffer, and the flexure may in particular be concentrated in an area not designed to submit to it. Fatigue failures of sidewall, clinch or bead areas may be shockingly premature where these limits are transgressed.

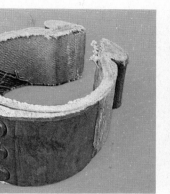
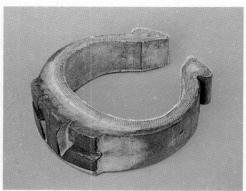
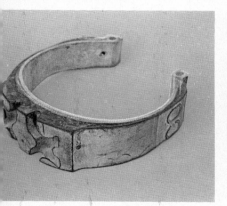

The relationship between rim width and tyre width is not immutable, but there are some sound general rules by which to abide. First note that the actual cross-sectional width of a tyre often differs from its nominal width: a 6.00V16 tyre, for example, is actually 7.2 inches wide when set on a 4½ inch rim. Next, note that an increase of half an inch in rim width will add a fifth of an inch to the tyre width. Now, allowing for all this, the rim should normally be at least 60 per cent as wide as the tyre, and preferably 70 per cent. Especially in the case of radial-ply tyres, it is better to err on the wide side, but 85 per cent should not normally be exceeded. Special tyres may demand different fittings: racing tyres sometimes have rims as wide as themselves, while most of the recent generation of 'safety' or 'run-flat' tyres are designed to fit narrow rims.

Best known of these is the Dunlop Denovo, a belted radial of low profile, designed so that when deflated it will allow itself to be distorted radially but not laterally. Thus the deliberately narrow rim specified for the special wheel falls closer to the ground until the bead area of the tyre makes contact with the inside of the tread area, cushioning the rim against the road; the friction likely to be generated there is abated by lubrication with a fluid secreted in capsules lodged within the tyre cavity and broken when the tyre goes down. The fluid contains a volatile component that then generates a vapour pressure of about four pounds per square inch which is enough to partly repressurize the tyre. With these aids the Denovo can be run in the post-deflation state for about one hundred miles at speeds of up to fifty miles an hour.

Capable of running without any internal pressurization at all, without relying on internal liquids and *without any carcass cords*, the prototype Pirelli triangular tyre is a signpost to a future in which tyres promise to be very different. Its sidewalls are a pair of incurved arches in compression, springing from a very narrow rim which firmly clasps their unwired bead ends, whilst the outer ends are connected and restrained by transverse tension in the tread belt which is the only reinforcement within the tyre. External applied loads, horizontal and vertical, are transmitted by the sidewalls acting as solid rubber compression springs; static load and inflation pressure both tend to prestress the sidewall arch so that it is always in compression, even when cornering. Furthermore, the shaping of the sidewalls and the characteristics of the rubber (much more accurately predictable in the absence of carcass cords) produce a non-linear response to loading, so the capacity of the tyre actually increases to meet any extra demands on it. For example in cornering, the lateral load compresses, thickens, and stiffens the opposing sidewall 'spring' in a progressive way that positively assists prompt and accurate steering.

The result is a tyre that gives an astonishingly soft ride and beautifully damped kick-free steering but yet combines outstanding adhesion and steering response with high cornering power—all without any material sensitivity to inflation pressure, camber, load or speed. It is a very squat tyre, being made initially as a 50 per cent aspect ratio tyre (that is, the distance from rim to road is half the width of the tyre) but capable of being made even lower in profile, down to about 10 per cent: this brings attractions of space saving, not only because the spare tyre is otiose, but because either wheel arches can be made smaller, or else the brakes and steering or suspension mechanisms can occupy more space inside the wheel.

More extraordinary facts continue to emerge. Perforating the sidewall has no effect: the compressive state closes the holes—so the conventional valve can be

eliminated, inflation being done through an hypodermic needle! Because there is no carcass to be hand-lasted as in a conventional tyre (in the manufacture of which there is a great deal of manual work), the thing can be processed almost entirely automatically, to the benefit of uniformity and therefore of ride—though, in any case, the tyre will itself absorb and damp any vibrations entering or engendered in it. Suspension can therefore be simpler because compliance (which isolates belt-induced vibrations from conventional tyres) will be unnecessary. The lack of camber sensitivity allows suspensions to be even simpler, to be much less expensive to manufacture and to require much less space. The conventional tyre has come an amazingly long way in about ninety years; inside another ten years what now appears to be a most unconventional tyre may be expected to supplant today's version. LJKS

Top left: Pirelli across the world

Top right: one of the earliest types of tyre, made in leather, which is primitive compared with the Pirelli run-flat tyre of 1974 *(centre)*; the triangular-section tyre requires a special wheel, as shown

Above: studs are fitted to many tyres used in snowy conditions for extraction

A SHREWD TALENT-SPOTTER

Ken Tyrrell has been the guiding light behind the career of many racing drivers, including Jackie Stewart and Jody Scheckter

THE NAME OF TYRRELL—like that of Ferrari, Porsche, and very few others of real significance—was famous in motor racing before it ever came to identify a racing car. Robert Kenneth Tyrrell, proprietor of a tree-felling business based in the woods at Ripley, Surrey (not for nothing is he known to some as 'Chopper' Tyrrell), took to motor racing as early as 1952, in the heyday of the 500 cc Formula Three. At the age of 28 he was no stranger to high-speed machinery, having served as a flight mechanic and engineer in the Royal Air Force, and he did not do badly in the years that followed, driving the inevitable Cooper-Norton. After 1957 he moved up to Formula Two in a Cooper-Climax team with Alan Brown and Cecil Libowitz; but in a short time he decided to retire from driving in races, finding more satisfaction and scope for his talents in the organisation of the team.

He picked good men to drive for him. Brabham, Ireland, Gregory and McLaren were among them, and by 1960 he had made a good enough impression to be entrusted with the management of the factory-backed Cooper team in the new Formula Junior. A year later he was in charge of the Mini-Cooper team as well, and when John Cooper was sidelined by a road accident Tyrrell held the Formula One reins in his absence.

Those were immensely successful days, in a period when motor sport was growing rapidly in popularity and professionalism, especially in Britain. Tyrrell the team manager acquired a particular reputation as a shrewd judge of driving talent, and the young hopefuls who queued up to come under his scrutiny were almost guaranteed a place in the limelight if he gave his approval. Just look at the list of names of his protégés: Ballisat, Banks, Love, Maggs, Procter, Taylor. . . .

. . .not to mention Scheckter, Stewart and Surtees. Perhaps Tyrrell was not right every time, but he seems to have been right when it mattered. His association

Left: Ken Tyrrell *(centre)* in conference during the 1974 British Grand Prix at Brands Hatch, an event won in fine style by the Elf Team Tyrrell 007 of South African Jody Scheckter

Below: in 1969, Jackie Stewart drove Ken Tyrrell's Matra MS80-Ford to victory in the World Championship, the first of three world titles that Stewart was to gain with Tyrrell

with Stewart was especially important, for the young Scot quickly became a red hot property, capable of attracting the most influential backing and doing justice to the most exceptional cars. They did not come his way immediately after Tyrrell gave him a private test drive at Goodwood in 1963, but by 1965 Stewart's value was confirmed in some scintillating drives for BRM, and

Above: after an unsuccessful early 1970 season campaigning March 701 cars, Ken Tyrrell introduced his own Tyrrell-Ford Formula One car; it was designed by Derek Gardner and used the well-proven Cosworth-Ford V8 3-litre engine

Right: Ken Tyrrell seen wearing his famous frown—or is it a smile?

overtures began to be made by Matra.

This led to even greater things the next year, when the amalgamation of French oil companies known as Elf entered the sponsorship lists as backers for Engins Matra. Tyrrell had been his usual shrewd self in 1967 when he saw the new Cosworth Ford V8 engine propel Lotus to victory in the Dutch GP on its first appearance, and he had ordered one forthwith, leaving the question of what to do with it to ponder later. In that same year Matra had been driving good bargains too, contriving a three-year loan of six million francs from the French government for the construction of a Formula 1 racer powered by a French engine.

Tyrrell had more than just Stewart. He had the promise of an engine from Ford for the 1968 season, and the support of Dunlop who were anxious to show that they were still as good at their job as Firestone or

Goodyear. Thus armed, Tyrrell went to Matra with a proposal for a Cosworth-engined Matra for Stewart to drive in the Grands Prix, the idea being that it would be a chance for Matra to hedge their bets (their own V12 was by no means a certain winner) and keep the French public happy. The result was the MS10 Matra, in which Stewart did so well that by the end of 1968 he was second in the championship points table. Tyrrell was now in a position from which he could bargain very strongly, and for 1969 he ran the Matra Elf International team: Stewart and Beltoise were his drivers, and so persuasive was he that Matra's engineer, Bernard Boyer, designed a car with the Cosworth engine specially for that season.

After winning six Grands Prix and his first world championship, Stewart might be thought to have justified Matra in a prolongation of their ties with Tyrrell. The French thought otherwise: Chauvin would have been proud of Matra, who insisted on concentrating on their own engine. Tyrrell and Stewart were equally insistent on sticking to the devil they knew. Much was made of the news that Stewart would be driving for Tyrrell in one of the first new March racers; but this publicity was deliberately fostered to draw attention away from the work that was being done in secret by the designer Derek Gardner at Tyrrell's behest. The entrant was wary of the fact that the March was an unknown quantity and he decided that the services of Stewart merited a car of his own.

In 1968 the team had toyed with a four-wheel-drive Matra, and in the course of working on this Tyrrell had come to know and admire the work of Gardner, who

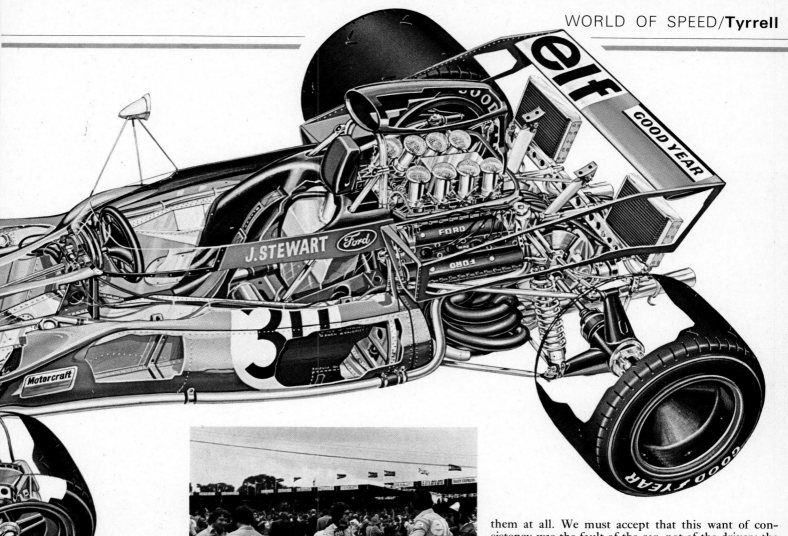

Above: a cutaway of Jackie Stewart's Tyrrell-Ford 003, as it appeared at the 1971 Italian GP at Monza. Sponsored by the French Elf company, it was designed by Derek Gardner and used a Ford-Cosworth DFV V8 engine and a Hewland FG 400 gearbox. The car was later put on display at Tom Wheatcroft's Donington Museum, before being presented to Stewart as a retirement present

Right: the Tyrrell 007 of Jody Scheckter sits on the grid at Silverstone prior to the start of the 1975 British Grand Prix. Scheckter was to know no joy, however, and ended his race against a bank after losing control during a heavy rain storm

had been working with the Ferguson four-wheel-drive specialists. Now he set the designer to work at a secret drawing board, from the surface of which the Tyrrell car was to spring. It was not to be altogether a leap in the dark: the Matra of 1968 had served Stewart very well indeed, and the Gardner car was to exhibit similar characteristics, with a low polar moment of inertia, a wide track, and craftsmanship of a very high order. This embodiment of established principles was proved to be sufficient to ensure satisfactory performance when Stewart, admittedly the most professional and one of the most proficient drivers of the time, began a very profitable run with this new car in 1970. The result was surprising only in the apparent ease with which the Tyrrell proved able on most occasions to trounce all the opposition—which made all the more surprising those occasions when it appeared unable to compete with

them at all. We must accept that this want of consistency was the fault of the car, not of the driver; the latter was always at pains to make this clear.

Teething troubles are forgiveable in any new car, and it was nothing worse than that which hampered the progress of the original Tyrrell after its successful start. Numbered 001, the car made its début in August 1960 and promptly set a new outright lap record at Oulton Park, which is (or was then) much more like genuine road-racing than some of the bloated arenas in which the sport is nowadays conducted. The car held a commanding lead in the Canadian GP before being forced to abate or abort; it enjoyed the same eminence in the United States GP when again it was toppled by fate. Nevertheless it was a good car, and the exhaustive testing programme upon which it embarked after the end of its first season led to a new chassis, number 003, being built for the 1971 series and proving so good that it was kept on for the following year.

In fact 003 was probably the most successful single car in the history of Grand Prix racing. With Stewart at the helm it won eight Grands Prix in 1971 and 1972, collecting the world championship for its driver in the former year. The second driver in the team, another Tyrrell protégé, took the American GP and third place in the drivers' championship: this was François Cevert, a youngster of considerable promise whom the team manager was careful to develop at a careful pace. The two drivers were a good team, being mutually complementary not only when working out race tactics but also in the development of the cars: Stewart had no peer as a judge of tyres, while Cevert was blessed with great sensitivity to variations in the aerodynamic equilibrium of the car. Stewart was the better able to adjust to the deterioration of his car's handling as the race progressed, but after a year or two under the combined Tyrrell-Stewart tutelage Cevert could on occasions

2419

show himself the faster when the car was right.

He should have had ample opportunity in 1972, for Stewart was kept away from the grids by illness during the earlier part of the season; but the Scot returned to scintillating form later in the year, while the Frenchman could reach no higher than sixth in the points table. The car was changed during the course of the year: when 005 came on the scene, it was shorter, lower, more rectilinear in shape and more pointed in its behaviour. In many ways it was a straightforward development of the earlier cars: its deep hammerhead nose was initially like that of 003, for example, although it soon changed to a shallower end-fenced design with a range of adjustments rivalling that of the simple diaplane on the nose of 001. The brakes were the most important departure: after experimenting fruitlessly with the double-disc Girling design at Monaco, Gardner decided to set the front brakes inboard in his new chassis, reaping all the benefits of reduced unsprung mass, larger disc size, better cooling, and unencumbered steering, in exchange for the nominally simple universally jointed shafts that linked discs to hubs. In fact, that simplicity was never quite achieved, for the combination of braking torque and suspension movement, with steering deflections superimposed, creates engineering difficulties that might be thought insuperable were it not that BRM never seemed to have any trouble with theirs. . . .

By the process of simple modifications and straightforward developments, 005 evolved into 006 for 1973. A rear wing carried further aft, large lateral radiators sprouting just ahead of the rear tyres, a tall engine-air tower, and a modified shape for the central 'monocoque' tub, were the most evident changes built into the car that won Stewart yet another world championship. It was beginning to look as though the Tyrrell system only worked at its best in odd-numbered years; but 1973 was by no means unalloyed in its joy for the team, for Cevert was killed, and Stewart in due course announced his decision to retire.

Tyrrell responded as calmly as ever to this new crisis in the team's affairs. He chose Scheckter and Depailler to form a completely new team for 1974, and set Gardner to the creation of a new car for them. Familiarity had enabled Stewart and Cevert to deal with the difficulties in the handling of 006 as they arose, for they were engaged all the time in its development. The newcomers had no such background, and Gardner was aware that the very fast responses of the short-wheelbase car, aggravated by pronounced pitch variations and difficulties in aerodynamic tuning, might offer obstacles to their progress. His answer was 007, six inches longer in the wheelbase and altogether a more complex construction than any earlier Tyrrell. The central tub was flat-surfaced, flanked by GRP pods containing the regulation deformable structure and also serving as ducts for the lateral water radiators. The extra length was inserted behind the driver, the space being occupied by an oil tank and bounded by a substantial roll-over hoop attached to the rear of the tub. Not only did this hoop stiffen the hull in torsion, it also offered a preferred anchorage for the engine bearers (the Cosworth DFV engine is still treated as a stressed chassis member) and for suspension pick-up points through which tractive and braking loads are fed into the chassis well away from the lateral and spring loads. Torsion bars replaced the helical rear springs of the earlier cars; at the front, the helical springs and their concentric dampers were again set inboard out of the way of the brakes on the chassis.

It was all beautifully made. There has never been a Tyrrell that was not. Nearly all British racing cars are

just like nearly all the other British racing cars, but few are as nicely put together, as meticulously finished or as thoughtfully conceived. Yet this is not the work of a giant corporation. The cars are built in the same yard that was shared by Formula Junior Coopers and timber trucks fifteen years ago. To be sure, the money is spent as though it came from a giant corporation, for Tyrrell admitted that half a million pounds were spent in 1973 and £600,000 in 1974, a sixth of that being tied up in eleven engines. Indeed, some of the money *does* come from a giant corporation, for Elf is a very big organisation indeed. Its name is still part and parcel of the Tyrrell racing show, the title Elf-Team Tyrrell celebrating what is claimed to be the longest standing sponsorship in Grand Prix racing, which is probably as effective a compliment to the managerial acumen of Mr Tyrrell as anything could be.

The 007 series of cars have maintained their early promise. Scheckter very nearly won the 1974 championship, and together with the polished Depailler has been going well in 1975. However, the team of thirty-odd individuals have more than the Formula One Grands Prix on their plate: in a casual things-to-come act they have been leaving the new V6-engined Renault-Gordini F2 car lying around where it can be seen, and the possibility that this engine could in turbocharged 1½ litre form propel a fresh generation of racers in 1976 ought not to be dismissed.   LJKS

Top: famous Belgian motoring journalist, Paul Frère, testing the Formula One Tyrrell 007

Centre: Frenchman Patrick Depailler in action driving his Tyrrell 007 at Dijon during the 1975 French Grand Prix. Depailler was drafted into the Tyrrell team at the beginning of 1974 and proved to be a competent driver

Bottom: Ken Tyrrell entered a third Tyrrell 007 for the 1975 French GP at Dijon and entrusted it to French-man Jean-Pierre Jabouille who brought it home in twelfth position

CONSISTENT & CONSERVATIVE

The solid and staid Unic cars were a far cry from the earlier sporting creations of their designer, Georges Richard

WHEN GEORGES RICHARD, who had founded the Georges Richard Cycle Company as far back as 1893, broke away from the Richard-Brasier company to establish, somewhat confusingly, the Georges Richard Company, he was determined to keep, in this new independent venture, to a one-model policy. Hence the new venture's alternative title of La Societe des Voitures Legères Unic.

There was, however, nothing utilitarian about the Unic car, which first appeared in the early part of 1905. Rated at 10/12 hp, it was a handsome little car which, with ploughshare wings and a *roi des belges* body, looked remarkably like a miniature Mercedes, though its 1798 cc engine only had two cylinders. One of the very first Unics, valued at Fr 10,000, was given as first prize in a Gordon Bennett sweepstake organised by the magazine *La Vie au Grand Air* in May 1905.

M Richard did not keep to his one-model policy for long: in 1906 he announced a four-cylinder Unic, the 16/20, of 2616 cc, which sold in England for £450 complete, £100 more than the smaller model. Another four, the 12/14, appeared in 1907; this 1944 cc monobloc-engined car became the basis of the most famous Unic of all, the taxi version. The power unit remained in profuction for around two decades, while the Unic taxicabs were in evidence on the streets of London long after the model had ceased production. In fact, the old 10/12 twin, which survived until 1911, ended its days as a taxi chassis, too: the National Motor Cab Company of Hammersmith ran a fleet of 250, the day-to-day running of which was supervised by a young man named W. O. Bentley.

Oddly enough, considering the sporting reputation of the Richard-Brasier, the Unic cars were dull and stodgy machines, and not particularly rewarding to drive. Engaging top gear, for example, was a tricky business, and likely to jar the driver's wrist if handled unskilfully. The Unic cabs were notoriously bad starters on cold mornings, and Bentley had to heat their plugs in a coke brazier like so many roast chestnuts in an effort to persuade them to fire.

The year 1908 saw a new big four added to the line-up: this was the 24/30, with a 3759 cc engine and a £500 price tag. A year later came a short-lived six-cylinder

Below: the competition Unic prior to the 1907 Criterium de la France
Bottom: 1909 Unic two-seater runabout

Above: a superbly restored and maintained Unic C7 series T 2-seater tourer of 1912

Right: a 1938 Unic U6B two-door coupé, with coachwork by Letourneum and Marchand; this was one of the last cars produced by Unic, before the company returned to the manufacture of commercial vehicles in 1939

model, the 4086 cc 25/35, which cost £620 in chassis form, but only survived in production until 1911. In any case, such ventures had become quite un-characteristic of the Unic, which was now firmly established as a taxi chassis: indeed, its then con-cessionaires, Mann & Overton of London, originally importers of high-priced luxury cars like the Mercedes, became identified with taxis as a result of their association with Unic—and are still prominent in that part of the automotive market.

Owners praised the uncomplaining reliability of the Unic. In 1912 Gilbert G. Blackman of Oxted, Surrey, wrote: 'The 12/14 hp Unic I bought in July 1910 is still going strong, and in spite of the fact that I have just ticked off another 10,000 miles the motor is as good as when delivered to me. The replacements during the whole of the time have amounted to 4s 6d. Although I live in an exceedingly hilly district, I am able to average 32 to 45 miles per gallon'.

By the outbreak of war, it seemed as though the old one-model policy was totally abandoned: an 8/10 hp 1206 cc twin had lasted only the 1912 season, and the 10/12 twin had been replaced at the end of 1913 by a new 1460 cc four, which was now the smallest of a five model range. The 16/24 hp of 3308 cc was a development of the 1906 model, but the rest was all new: there was a 2614 cc 12/18 hp four and a longstroke big four of 23/40 hp and 6242 cc, while a six once more appeared in the range in the shape of the positively ephemeral 19/35 hp of 3921 cc. But the war changed all that.

Unics of the 1919–21 period were remarkable only for their complex double cantilever rear suspension, and in 1922 came a new 1847 cc four, the Type L, with equally curious back springing by a single cantilever above a short quarter-elliptic spring. This was the last new model developed under Georges Richard, who was killed in an accident in June 1922, aged 59.

The Type L had unit construction of engine and gearbox, and four-wheel braking as early as 1922. Though its construction was otherwise conventional, it was apparent that Unic were trying to slough off the old taxi image with this model, for handsome sporting

versions were available, culminating in the 70 mph 2-litre ohv 11CV Type L3T3 Sport of 1923–25, which was seemingly the first car to bear horizontal bonnet louvres: automotive stylists had arrived!

By 1926 only this 2 litre 11CV model was available, in touring or sporting form, which showed that Unic had at last returned to its origins. But this singleness of purpose was submerged in a new consortium between ailing manufacturers which took place in 1927, when Unic, Chenard-Walcker and Delahaye linked up to

rationalise their resources. Rosengart became part of this *groupement* in 1929, but by that time the partners had already started to go off on their own separate ways once more.

In 1929, Unic again abandoned their single-model policy, announcing two straight-eights with overhead valves and four forward speeds alongside the 11 CV. These cars had a new form of rear suspension—by double cantilevers of unequal lengths.

But this was nothing to the curious front suspension adopted by Unic in 1934, after, it seems, a period in the economic doldrums when no cars were built. Reported *The Motor*'s correspondent at the Paris Salon: 'Unic, after an absence of several years, present an interesting display of new cars, and this firm, like Peugeot, has adopted the "one colour" idea. All the Unic cars are finished in white with red leather upholstery. Intensely conservative in design, the new Unic cars nevertheless follow the trend towards independent suspension which has become universal on the continent. The Unic suspension arrangement retains the classic, half-elliptic spring, but the chassis is carried by articulated arms, bolted to the centre of the spring and hinged at the opposite side of the frame, all of which combines to form a two-part "axle".'

The year 1936 saw the adoption of a horizontal handbrake projecting from the dashboard and alloy cylinder heads. *The Motor* commented: 'Unic, who returned to the touring car world last year after concentrating for some time on industrial vehicles only, present two entirely new chassis, a 2-litre and a 3-litre. The most interesting is a sports version of the 3-litre. This has an overhead valve pushrod engine with an aluminium cylinder head, and a feature of the chassis is the double-reduction gear in the rear axle'. This gave a low overall height without a transmission tunnel.

Other features of the new models were an oil cooler incorporated in the radiator and Cotal electric gearboxes. According to *The Autocar*: 'The complete cars are less advanced in their appearance than the majority of French cars, and are, therefore, more nearly in accord with British ideas. The four-door, four-light saloon, for example, is a well-balanced design with a large luggage trunk and sweeping well-balanced wings, and might be taken for a British car.'

Which, it seems, spelt economic disaster on the French market. Unic's return to the touring car industry was short-lived, and in 1939 they once again turned to the production of commercial vehicles. Still listed when private car output ceased was the old 11 CV (though now they called it a 12) a reminder of the days in 1923 when it was introduced.   DBW

WHATEVER IS IT?

So few Unipowers were made that their appearance on a public road is guaranteed to cause interest and speculation

LIKE THE AUSTIN SEVEN, generations before, the Mini lent itself as a sound basis for many specialist home-made sports cars. The ease with which the front sub-frame could be removed and inserted into a new chassis, which itself could be clothed in many bodies, meant that those seeking 'something different' could easily conjure it up. There was no need to design engines and transmissions, that was already being taken care of by British Motor Corporation.

Of the many BMC-based home-made cars and vehicles turned out by the numerous small companies, quick to realise the public's need, probably the best known and undoubtedly the most successful was the Unipower.

The Unipower project began in 1963 when two people, Ernest Unger and Val Dare-Bryan met at a race meeting, got talking and decided that they had the same ambition: to build a small, cheap mid-engined sports car. Rough thoughts and ideas were finally converted into drawings for a prototype, by an anonymous (for obvious reasons) stylist at Fords who entered the project. In 1964 the first aluminium body was placed on the spaceframe chassis designed by Unger and Dare-Bryan.

At an early stage, it was decided that the best engine/transmission option would be that of the Mini, and it was placed in the car. The unit was inserted transversely in the chassis just in front of the rear-axle line. Everything fitted nicely, except that the gearbox was the 'wrong way round'. This meant that the gearlever was on the right-hand side *a la* racing sports car. However, the slight problem was that the only way the gearlever could work the gears was by having the gate back to front, ie, first towards the driver and second away from him; a little dangerous for the uninitiated driving off in a hurry! The car, incidentally, was built at racing driver Roy Pierpoint's workshop.

Although Pierpoint was enthusiastic over the car, financiers Tim Powell and Andrew Hedges decided to take the project over. Powell, a well known powerboat racer, was in charge of a company called Universal Power Drives of Perivale, Middlesex, who built forestry tractors for such jobs as towing trees and stripping them of bark. By November of 1965, Powell has set aside space in his factory for producing the car, which now was to be clothed in glassfibre, courtesy of the redoubt-able Specialised Mouldings Company.

In January 1966 the début of the car was at the

Above: a rear three-quarter view of the tiny Unipower GT; the car was powered by a BMC Mini engine fitted amidships and driving the rear wheels; it used a spaceframe chassis

Far left: the Unipower was extremely low, as can be gauged by this picture of the car alongside a truck wheel

Left: the Unipower's BMC engine was fitted transversely in front of the rear axle and could be reached by tilting the glassfibre rear body section

Right: a Unipower GT with a difference—this was the only example ever made with left-hand-drive

Racing Car Show in two forms: coupé and Targa top. Incidentally, it is worth noting that the car was originally to be called the Hustler GT, a name later associated with a popular beach buggy. The response to the little mid-engined car was great, but there was still much development necessary. Such things as the rear-mounted radiator had to be adjusted and, in this case, moved to the front of the car, whilst the wind-up windows were replaced by the Mini sliding type.

By the time the 1967 Racing Car Show came around, few models had been built, and what few existed were

based on the coupé, the Targa version being dropped in favour of the easier-to-produce closed car.

The '67 Show saw the car as it was to appear in production. As previously mentioned, the Unipower was based on the Mini engine and transmission, in either Cooper or Cooper S form. The car's spaceframe chassis was built by Specialised Moulding's neighbours Arch Motors, the completed unit being sent to Perivale for trimming and assembly. Standing a might over 40 inches, the Unipower was seated on all independent suspension by way of the simple but effective double-wishbone and coil-spring system, set up with negative camber at both ends. In component form, the Cooper-engined car cost £950, while the 1275 cc S-powered car cost a trifling £1145.

With, or even despite of, 40 per cent front, 60 per cent rear weight distribution, the car had remarkably good roadholding and handling. The way the tail of the car could be hung out allied its handling to that of a Kart; indeed, the size of the vehicle meant that it could sometimes be mistaken for one of its solid-tyred contemporaries! As for performance, the 998 cc car had a top speed of 104 mph and could accelerate from 0–60 mph in 12.5 secs, while the 1275 cc car had a top speed of 115 mph and accelerated to 60 mph from rest in 9.5 secs. Fuel consumption worked out at approximately 34 and 29 mpg respectively for the two cars.

Under the guidance of Andrew Hedges, a few Unipowers were put onto race tracks but even with the aid of a few aerodynamic devices to combat wander at high speed, they proved mediocre. Not all were BMC powered, though. One car, driven by Stanley Robinson, had a Formula Two Cosworth FVA engine to propel it.

Back to production cars. Throughout 1967 and '68, production of the Unipower continued, although Tim Powell was slowly losing interest in the project. Then, along came Piers Weld-Forrester to take things over at a new factory in Willesden. Up until that time, about sixty cars had been produced and, to try and boost sales, a Mk II version was instigated with a higher standard of finish and better standard equipment. The new car had

different softer-rate springs, a tidied-up rear end and a neater cockpit. By now, a five-speed gearbox was offered as an option, too. However, after another part of a season was spent preparing a carbon-fibre-bodied racer, things started to turn sour. Between 1968 and '69, plans were put forward for new models, one with a Triumph Stag engine and another with the proposed 2.2-litre, six-cylinder BMC engine. The latter car, designed by Peter Bohanna, became the Maxi-engined Diablo, which itself became the AC3000, but that is a different story. The Unipower story, however, was reaching its finale. The money spent on the racing project was money that should have been spent on the road car's development, and by January 1970 the company was wound up. In the last phase of production under Weld-Forrester, about fifteen cars were built.

So, seven years after the car was first conceived, production ceased, and the pretty little road-hugger was left to be mourned by many and much sought after by people who either wanted an appreciating asset or by those who wanted an economical and exhilerating sports car, and were prepared to answer the inevitable question: 'Whatever is it?'   LJC

Top : a 1969 Unipower GT being driven at Mugello in Italy by Piers Weld-Forester and Dominique Martin

Above: Andrew Hedges (wearing spectacles), posing with this Unipower GT and three of the men who helped to build it

DRIVE FROM ANY ANGLE

The universal joint enables motion to be transmitted from one rotating shaft to another, even when the two are not in line

ENGINE TORQUE HAS TO BE SMOOTHLY TRANSMITTED to roadwheel axles that are continually but irregularly tilting due to road unevenness, twisting due to drive and brake torque reaction and, in some vehicles, turning to and fro as the wheels are steered.

As the result of this varied motion both the angle of drive to the axle and its distance relative to the gearbox or final drive unit are constantly changing. To meet these circumstances a universal joint or joints combined with either a telescopic propellor shaft (prop shaft) or short solid drive shafts are normally employed. The complete assembly is referred to as a drive line.

The principle of transmitting rotary motion from one shaft placed at an angle to another by means of a universal joint was solved very many years ago by Hooke and Cardan. Their joint used two yokes on planes perpendicular to each other and pivotally connected by a control block (spider) fitted with cross pins.

Early types of universal joints for cars included the globe joint, in which forks on two shafts fitted into two grooves cut at right angles in a steel ball, and discs, made up of leather or, more lately, rubberised fabric. These discs formed a flexible joint between two shafts, being attached to each shaft by three bolts spaced alternately around the disc.

A modern Hooke's joint consists of two yokes, a spider journal (also known as a cross pin or cross piece), four needle bearings which support the journal within the lugs (or ears) of the yokes, and four circlips or snap rings which retain the needle bearings in place; although sometimes the yoke is peened over to retain the bearings (*staked type*). Some older models had bronze bushes instead of needle roller bearings.

The output velocity of a Hooke's type joint fluctuates twice per revolution, the extent of the fluctuation depending on the angle between the driving and driven shafts. This is because, as the joint rotates, one pair of cross pins follows the plane of rotation of the driven yoke so that the attitude of this intermediate member is continually changing. At a joint angle of 28 degrees the speed variation may be as high as 25 per cent, so that in practice the maximum joint angle is limited to 18 degrees to 20 degrees on either side of the zero (or in-line) position.

This irregularity in velocity transmission is overcome by using a double joint or two separate joints connected by a shaft. At the second joint there is a similar variation in velocity, but providing the planes of the two joints are exactly aligned, and the angle of the driving shaft and the driven shaft to the connecting shaft are equal, the variation at the second joint is equal and opposite to that which occurs at the first, and consequently cancels it out to give a uniform speed at the final drive.

Thus a double Hooke's joint is perfectly satisfactory for in-line front engine, rear wheel drive vehicles and it is widely used today. Difficulties arose, however, as other engine/drive wheel layouts were developed, particularly with front or rear engined units driving directly on to the front or rear wheels respectively. It was found that there was insufficient space and the drive angle was too great for Hooke's joints.

One of the first practical solutions to the problem, the constant velocity joint, was evolved by A. H. Rzeppa in 1926. He applied the fundamental principle that, for an output velocity faithfully to reproduce the input velocity, an intermediate member must be maintained at all times in a plane (the *median plane*) which bisects the angle between the driving and the driven shafts. Rzeppa's solution was to employ a 'ball and socket' joint with an intermediate member, for transmitting the torque, made up of six steel balls. The 'ball' and 'socket'

were each grooved to accommodate the separate balls, which were retained in a special cage forming the median plane.

The modern continuous velocity joint is based on the Rzeppa principle, but some improvements have been

Below: gearbox output shafts, with rubber joints built-in between the shaft and the connecting flange

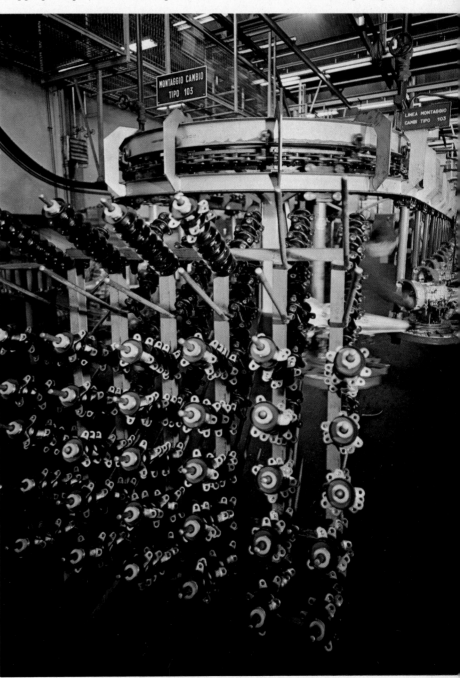

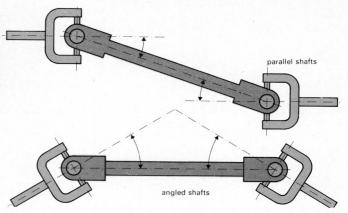

parallel shafts

angled shafts

Hooke's joints are used on most propeller shafts, although they are not so popular in drive shafts, because the speed of the driven shaft is not constant and the variation has to be cancelled out by a second joint; as long as the angles of the shafts (x) are equal and the shafts parallel, the variations are equal and opposite; otherwise, they become greater

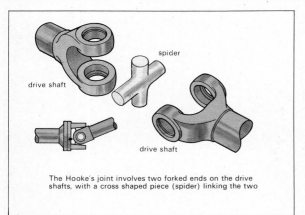

spider

drive shaft

drive shaft

The Hooke's joint involves two forked ends on the drive shafts, with a cross shaped piece (spider) linking the two

made, chiefly that of having an elliptical, instead of circular, section for the ball tracks, thereby improving the 'conformity ratio'; this means that the contact points of the balls are always located to the best advantage. The joint transmits constant speed over a wide angle, so that only one joint per drive line is normally required. A variation of the constant velocity joint incorporates a limited 'plunge', giving lateral movement up to $2\frac{1}{2}$ inches (75 mm). This type of joint is particularly useful with independent wheel suspensions. Its efficiency, 100 per cent at zero drive angle, drops only to 96 per cent at an angle of 40 degrees, although the vehicle design does not normally require it to exceed 30 degrees.

There are a great many combinations of universal joints, single and split propellor shafts, drive shafts and rubber couplings to be found in modern drive lines. Some joints—so-called 'pot joints' (grease packed and sealed in rubber covers)—and other covered joints may

not at first even be recognised for what they are. Typical drive line layouts include the following.

With a front, in-line engine driving the rear wheels the usual arrangement is for a Hooke's type universal joint located immediately behind the gearbox to be connected by the propellor shaft to a second Hooke's joint mounted in front of the differential casing. One variation of this arrangement is the divided, or split, propellor shaft. The front section, supported towards its rear end by a rubber-mounted bearing attached to the underside of the body, is driven from the gearbox by a rubber coupling. The rear section has the usual Hooke's type joint at each end. This split shaft overcomes the tendency to whip that might become apparent on a long shaft, and allows the floor of the car to be lowered. The purpose of the rubber coupling and bearing support is to dampen out vibrations and to absorb the initial drive take-up shock.

The propellor shaft is usually a steel tube, between 2 in and 3 in (50 and 75 mm) in diameter. The varying distance between the rear axle and the gearbox is accommodated by manufacturing the shaft in two parts with splined ends, one part sliding in the other.

With a front engine and rear wheel drive, the rear axle half shafts are sometimes replaced by drive shafts with a Hooke's type universal joint at each end. This system gives the wheels complete freedom to rise and fall independently while the drive is maintained.

With front engine, front wheel drive and rear engine, rear wheel drive, the usual arrangement is for a constant velocity joint to be fitted on the outboard (road wheel end) of a short drive shaft. Between the inboard end of the drive shaft and the final drive unit a rubber coupling is fitted. This may take the form of a rubber 'doughnut' or a rubber encased spider secured by four U-bolts. This coupling is sufficiently flexible to absorb suspension movements and drive take-up shock.

When drive line defect occur they make themselves known by vibration and unusual noises when the vehicle is in motion, particularly when slackness in the drive line is taken up on acceleration. With worn outboard constant velocity joints, knocking noises will be apparent when driving on near or full lock.
Points to check are:
a) Worn propellor shaft splines at the sliding joint—check by grasping each side of the joint and trying to twist in alternate, opposite directions. Any movement is indicative of wear, and a new shaft is necessary.
b) Bent propellor shaft—this will cause excessive vibration and throw a great strain on the universal joints.
c) Worn universal joint needle bearings—check by grasping the shafts on each side of the joint as for spline wear. Alternatively, a screwdriver can be inserted between the spider and the yoke and levered to detect movement.
d) On rubber couplings and disc type joints—check for

Below left: the spider elements used in Hooke's joints; roller bearings placed in caps on each of the four ends allow the drive shaft forks to pivot freely

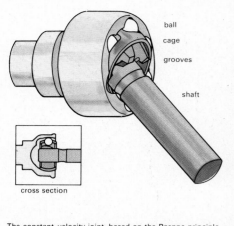

ball

cage

grooves

shaft

cross section

The constant-velocity joint, based on the Rzeppa principle, eliminates the problem, encountered in the Hooke's joint, of varying output velocity

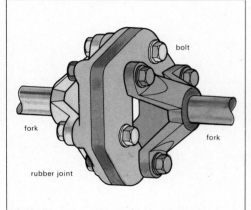

bolt

fork

fork

rubber joint

Rubber universal joints give limited angle change, but keep the shaft velocity constant; as can be seen, the three flanges of each shaft are bolted to the rubber 'doughnut' at equal intervals. The metal band round the outside is removed after the joint has been fitted

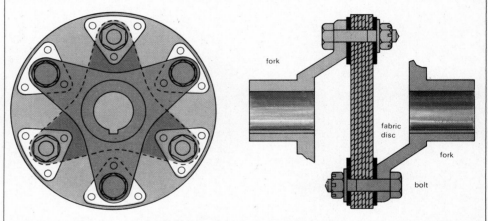

fork

fabric disc

fork

bolt

A cross section through an older type of flexible universal joint, using fabric instead of rubber. The arrangement of the forked drive-shaft ends is the same as for the 'doughnut' type, but the maximum possible angle difference is even smaller (3–5° instead of 5–6°)

splits, loose nuts and bolts, oval wear of the bolt holes, and deterioration due to contact with oil.

e) Lack of lubrication—on both the telescopic shaft joints and needle bearings or bushes—which will be evidenced by vibration coupled with squeaks.

f) Propellor shaft centre bearing—check for play and for soundness of any rubber anti-vibration support.

If no lubrication points are fitted to the joints it may be assumed that the bearings are packed with lubricant and 'sealed for life'. Otherwise, a lithium based grease is best used for needle bearings. Splined shafts require lubrication as well which is specified in the manufacturer's handbook.

Propellor and drive shafts are very carefully balanced and it is essential, if replacement becomes necessary, that they are replaced in the same position relative to the gearbox and final drive flanges, and that the two sections of a split shaft are similarly treated. Marks are normally provided on the shafts and flanges and these must always coincide (or be positioned as stated in the manufacturer's handbook) on replacement. If there are no marks, they should be scribed on the components before dismantling commences.

If the joints are of the Hooke's staked type, they can be replaced only as complete units. If, however, the bearing ends have circlips or snap rings, replacement parts are available as kits consisting of the spider journal, needle bearings and securing rings. If grease nipples are fitted on the old joint they should be

transferred to the new. Replacement of 'pot joints' may involve dismantling the final drive and the manufacturer's handbook should be consulted.

If no pit is available, the rear of the car should be jacked up and lowered onto stout support blocks. After top gear is engaged and the handbrake applied so that the propeller shaft does not turn. Loosen the four bolts uniting the propeller shaft and final drive flanges. Remove these bolts and push the propellor shaft forward to seperate the flanges. Then, lower the end of the shaft and pull it rearwards to disengage the splines.

Where a centre bearing is fitted, separate the centre universal joint flanges and remove the rear section of the shaft. Now separate the front flanges, dismantle the centre bearing and remove the front section of the shaft.

To dismantle the joint itself, remove the securing rings then, with a leather mallet, gently tap the yokes in turn; it will be found that the needle bearing races will eventually emerge.

To fit a new joint, place the spider journal in the yoke holes, grease the bearings and lightly tap them in from outside. Fit new securing rings.

If wear is apparent on a constant velocity joint, the whole joint must be replaced. Removal procedure varies from one vehicle to another, but usually a castellated nut locks the joint in place and a hub puller is required to remove it. On replacement the nut must be tightened with a torque wrench to the recommended figure.   AGH

Pike's people

AL AND BOBBY UNSER are both double Indianapolis winners. Both have been winners at Pike's Peak hillclimb, a venue which was almost considered the property of two generations of the Unser family. Both have tried road-racing in addition to their *forté*, the USAC National Championship trail. And both are deadly rivals.

The Unser family, with origins in Switzerland, are legendary in American motor racing circles. Their father, Jerry, raced from time to time before retiring in 1934. So did their two uncles. One, Louis—nicknamed 'Old Man Mountain'—competed at Pike's Peak and won nine times. He last raced there in 1967 at the age of 71. The other uncle, Joe, was killed there in 1929. There were four Unser brothers. The eldest were twins, Jerry and Louis. Jerry's Kuzma-Offenhauser hit the wall in the 1959 Indianapolis 500 and caught fire, the 26-year-old driver succumbed to serious burns two weeks later. As a result of the accident drivers were made to wear fire-resistant clothing. Louis won the stock car category at Pike's Peak in 1960 and 1961, but subsequently fell victim to multiple sclerosis and became involved with building competition boat engines.

Bobby was born on February 10, 1934, and Al on May 29, 1939. Both were affected by Jerry's accident. Bobby's trademark since has been his flat-out driving style, one that has resulted in engine blow-ups and crashes as well as victories. Al, taught to race by Bobby, developed a more analytical approach.

Bobby Unser began racing modified stock cars in 1949 at the age of 15. He won the New Mexico modified stock car championship in both 1950 and 1951 and then graduated to midgets and sprint cars. In 1956 he won the championship car division of the demanding 12½-mile Pike's Peak hillclimb, a demanding dirt road in the Rocky

Mountains of Colorado. In 1957 he was fifth and from 1958 won it six times in succession. Brother Al broke his string of victories in 1964. Bobby won again in 1966, 1968 and 1974. In all he had twelve wins at Pike's Peak, nine times in championship cars, once in a sports car and twice in stock cars.

In 1963 Bobby had his first taste of the Indianapolis 500, driving one of Andy Granatelli's fabulous 837 bhp supercharged Novis, extremely quick but unlucky machines. He qualified at sixteenth fastest and had rocketed to tenth before crashing into the wall on lap 3. For 1964 Unser handled a specially-commissioned four-wheel-drive Novi with a Ferguson P104 chassis, but retired early again after suffering minor burns running through a wall of

THE WINNER

blazing fuel on the track. The next year, Unser was handily-placed until an oil line broke on the 69th of the 200 laps.

A move was made to a turbocharged Offenhauser-engined Huffaker for the 1966 race, but Bobby only managed eighth. For 1967 he raced an Offy-engined Eagle for Bob Wilke, finishing ninth at Indianapolis following a six-minute pit-stop.

The 1968 season was Bobby Unser's greatest, highlighted with victory in the Indianapolis 500 in the Wilke-entered Eagle-Offenhauser. It was a surprise win, Joe Leonard's leading Lotus 56-Pratt & Witney turbine failing with a mere nine of the 200 laps to run. In practice, however, Unser had become the first person to lap the 2½-mile Indianapolis Motor Speedway at over 170 mph, registering 170.778 mph. Earlier in the year he had placed fifth at Hanford, first at Las Vegas, Phoenix and Trenton; after Indy he suffered occasional sour luck and the outcome of the USAC National Championship depended on the final round at Riverside. Bobby was a safe second to Dan Gurney and won the title by the narrow margin of 6.8 points—4326 to Mario Andretti's 4319.2.

In 1969 Unser raced the four-wheel-drive Lola T152-Offenhauser at Indianapolis, finishing third in the difficult-to-handle car. Back in an Eagle, he won the Langhorne 150, but in the latter part of the season he had to give best to his brother Al. . . . It was the same story in 1970, except for Langhorne where Bobby beat Al by a second after charging to the front in the closing minutes. Al won at Phoenix and in the Trenton 300 and Ted Horn 100. Eleventh was his Indianapolis placing in an Eagle-Ford. The following season, racing a works Olsonite Eagle-Offenhauser, Bobby led almost every USAC National Championship race only for mechanical failure to intervene. His only bright spot was victory in the Trenton 200 where he beat Mario Andretti by no less than two laps at a record average of 140.771 mph.

It was the same story in 1972. Unser had the fastest car in his works Eagle-Offenhauser. He had seven pole positions in succession to prove it. But again his car flattered only to deceive. He registered only four wins, two at Phoenix, one at Trenton and one at Wisconsin. In 1973 Unser's luck was again down, with only a repeat win in the Rex Mays 150 at Wisconsin to show for Bobby's efforts. But next season his luck turned. He appeared to play more of a waiting game, coming into the competition in the closing stages of a race. He won the Californian 500 at Ontario Motor Speedway and continued with victories in the Trentonian 200, the Michigan 200 and the Trenton Times 300 to clinch the USAC National Championship for the second time in his career.

Bobby Unser won the Indianapolis 500 for the second time in 1975 and pushed his USAC earnings over the £1 million mark. He also ran in some Formula 5000 races in the turbocharged

Opposite page: Al Unser, younger of the two famous Unser brothers, posing in the 1971 Indianapolis 500-winning Lightning Special

This page: Bobby Unser and the 1975 Indy 500-winning Jorgensen Eagle; Bobby also drove an Eagle to victory in the 1968 Indy 500

Eagle-Offenhauser and underlined the fact he could be competitive on road courses as well as oval tracks.

Al Unser began racing at the age of 18, racing Supermodified cars from 1957 to 1963. His business, however, was the running of a scrap yard which his father had purchased for him. In 1960 he ran at Pike's Peak for the first time, finishing second to Bobby. He was runner-up to his elder brother again in 1962, but in 1964 he broke the hill record *and* Bobby's run of six successive victories. In 1964 he entered the world of USAC racing, competing in both the Sprint and National Championship divisions, and the following season saw him tackle that pinnacle of American motor racing, the Indianapolis 500. Al passed his rookie's driving test in a machine entered by the Arciero brothers and powered by a Maserati engine, but the Italian unit blew up and as there was no spare it seemed Al would not make the official qualification runs. At the last minute he was offered a ride in A. J. Foyt's back-up Lola T80-Ford, qualified 32nd on the 33-car grid and soldiered through to finish ninth. His only win that year was at Pike's Peak.

In 1966 Unser offered his services to Lotus, who had a vacancy alongside '65 winner Jim Clark in the STP-backed works team of Lotus 38-Ford. Al climbed as far as third place before crashing. In other USAC National Championship events he was second in the Hoosier Grand Prix, the Trenton 200 and the Phoenix 200, finishing fifth in the points table. In 1967, as number two to Jackie Stewart in the John Mecom Lola T90-Ford team, Al finished second in the Indianapolis 500. In this team he began to work with George Bignotti, the famed preparer of USAC cars.

First USAC win for Al Unser came in 1968—the year brother Bobby won the Indianapolis 500—when he won at Nazareth on a mile dirt-track. He later won two races at Indianapolis Raceway Park (a separate track to the Indianapolis Motor Speedway) and two at Langhorne. At Indianapolis he escaped injury when his four-wheel-drive Lola T150-Ford lost a wheel and was destroyed when it hit the wall.

For 1969 the Al Unser/George Bignotti partnership joined with Vel Miletich and Parnelli Jones, who fielded a new Lola T152-Ford for Unser to drive at Indianapolis. After setting rapid practice times he fell off a motorcycle fooling with Jones and broke his leg. Angry with himself, he put his all into his racing when he returned to the tracks later in the year. He won five of the final six races in the USAC National Championship—at Milwaukee, Sacramento (with broken suspension), Seattle, Phoenix and DuQuoin—and was a close second in the sixth at Riverside to Mario Andretti. Despite his curtailed season, Unser was second in the championship trail.

There was no stopping Al Unser in 1970. Racing the Bignotti-developed Colt, based on a Lola, Unswer won at Phoenix, was second at Sears Point, third at Trenton and then won the Indianapolis 500. It was the highlight of his career, at a time when brother Bobby's fortunes were in the doldrums. And like Bobby in '68, Unser went on to take the USAC National Championship, winning ten of the eighteen rounds. He won at Indianapolis Raceway Park, won on the Springfield, DuQuoin, Sedalia and Sacramento dirt tracks, won at Milwaukee by a margin of three laps and conquered brother Bobby in the Trenton 300. In the inaugural California 500 at the Ontario Motor Speedway, Unser would have won again if his turbocharged had not failed only fourteen laps from the finish.

Once again racing Vel's Parnelli Colt-Ford, Unser began the 1971 season on top form. He won the opening USAC National Championship round at Rafaela in Argentina and hammered brother Bobby at Phoenix. Then he won the Indianapolis 500 for the second year in succession, driving a confident race and never dropping lower than fourth throughout the 200 laps.

In 1972 the Vel's Parnelli team fielded new Maurice Phillippe-designed VPJ-001 cars for a formidable array of three former USAC Champions, Mario Andretti, Joe Leonard and Al Unser. It was a disappointing year for Al. He failed to win a single championship race, best place being second in the Indianapolis 500, while his brother won four races.

The 1973 season began well with victory in the Texas 200 in April, but the new Offy-engined Vel's Parnelli VPJ-002s suffered from understeering problems as well as gearbox and engine failures and Al failed to win another USAC National Championship round. Most galling was his luck in the California 500 at Ontario. He was a contender for the lead until the closing minutes when the gearbox broke. Some consolation was his clinching of the three-race USAC National Dirt Track Championship from team-mate Andretti. A change to the ubiquitous Eagle chassis brought better fortune in 1974, Al winning the Norton 250 at Michigan and taking sufficient place results—including second to brother Bobby in the California 500—to be fourth in the end-of-season points table Unser also added another string to his bow, racing in Formula 5000 in late 1974 and 1975 and proving to be a strong contender.

A favourite American parlour game in recent years has been to argue which of the Unser brothers is the better. Some go for Bobby's speed and guts; others for Al's impassive, calculated approach. On the track there's nothing between them, and although good friends, they are deadly rivals until the chequered flag drops.   MK

Below: Bobby Unser's Eagle undergoes a pit-stop on its way to winning the 1975 Indianapolis 500 race; overseeing the operation is former Grand Prix star Dan Gurney, founder of the Eagle racing team

DISCOVERING A NEW WORLD

For years, the USAC has been promoting oval-track racing, a sport totally alien to the European motor-sport enthusiast

THE 1955 MOTOR RACING SEASON was one of the grimmest on record. The Le Mans accident, in which 82 people died, had repercussions throughout the world. These extended to the other side of the world when, in August, two months following the tragedy, the American Automobile Association ceased to sanction motor sport in the United States of America, stating it was too dangerous. Almost overnight the chief interests of the AAA—the running of the Indianapolis 500-mile race and the supervision of land speed record attempts—were taken over by a new organisation, the United States Auto Club.

The USAC was formed at a public meeting at the State Fairgrounds at Indianapolis with Thomas W. Binford as President, a position he was to hold for the next twelve years. Naturally the new organisation took control of the running of the Indianapolis 500. (This involved the enforcement of rules and regulations plus supervision of practice runs, drivers' tests, qualifications runs and the actual race.) In addition, the USAC sanctioned the Pike's Peak Hillclimb, the Mobilgas Economy Run, record attempts on the salt flats and increased the programme of midget racing and USAC National Championship events. The USAC has also sanctioned midget car racing, stock cars, sprint cars and, from time to time, road-racing machinery.

The USAC, together with the Sports Car Club of America, the National Association for Stock Car Racing (NASCAR) and, finally, the National Hot Rod Association—the four largest sanctioning organisations in the United States—formed a joint committee, the Automobile Competition Committee for the United States–FIA (ACCUS)—in 1957. It became the American representative of the world governing body, the FIA. The combined front has not always worked. The three members concerned with motor racing—the USAC, SCCA and NASCAR—are each jealous of their branch of the sport. Disagreements over permitting a driver from one club to participate in the activities of another have occurred on several occasions.

Lifeblood of the United States Auto Club is its midget racing. Introduced in 1933, and sanctioned by the AAA the following year, this class of racing is usually run on dirt or paved tracks ranging from one-tenth of a mile to a full mile. Cars must have a wheelbase between 66 and 76 in and their engines are limited to a maximum of 1868 cc for overhead-valve units or 2540 cc for 'stock-blocks'.

In 1974 there were 41 races scheduled for the USAC Midget Division. Championship winner was Mel Kenyon, a 41-year-old exponent from Lebanon, Indiana, who won four of the events, and placed fifteen other times in the top five. Kenyon was also champion in 1964, 1967 and 1968, becoming the first driver in midget history to win the series four times. Shorty Templeman (1956–58) and Jimmy Davies (1960–62) have won the championship three times. Prize funds range from $1705 to $7494 during the 1974 season, way

Below: Mario Andretti in action in the Lola T332 F5000 machine run by former USAC star Parnelli Jones. The 1975 American F5000 series was organised jointly by the USAC and the SCCA who, until the mid 1970s, had been jealous rivals, the United States Automobile Club, however, is known for oval track racing, although it is rapidly making its mark in road-racing

Right: Troy Ruttman and the 1957 John Zink Special; Ruttman was so keen to race that he even faked his birth certificate; at nineteen he was the Indianapolis Speedway's youngest driver

Far right: Pat O'Connor's Sumar Special of 1957. O'Connor was a product of Sprint and Midget car racing; he was killed at Indianapolis in 1958 in a first lap pile-up

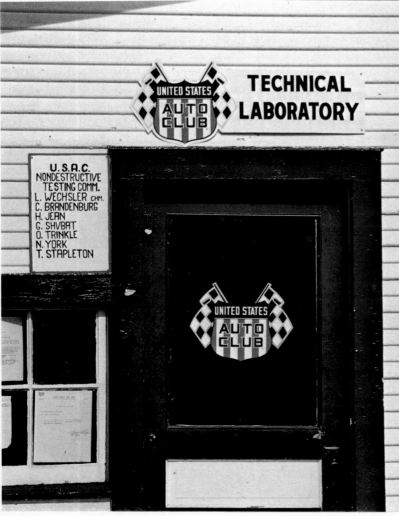

Above: the USAC's technical laboratory at Indianapolis is one of the best equipped in the world

off the 1969 Astro Grand Prix record of $60,000 at Houston, Texas.

The midgets set many well-known Indianapolis stars on the road to glory, as did the sprint cars. A step up the ladder, the sprint cars are great crowd-pullers. They mostly run on the same type of tracks as the midgets, but are bigger (84 in wheelbase) and powered by more powerful, larger engines (4200 cc for normally-aspirated racing units with other sizes for stock block and supercharged engines).

The 1974 sprint car season featured 34 races, the majority on half-mile circuits, both dirt and paved. Purses ranged from $7475 to $35,907. The 1974 champion was Duane Carter Jr who won seven rounds, took six seconds, one third, five fourths, two fifths and a sixth. Since 1961, first year of the USAC National Sprint Car Championship, no one has won the title more than twice. Double winners have been rare, but Parnelli Jones, Roger McCluskey, Larry Dickson, and Gary Bettenhausen have managed the feat.

Stock-car racing is chiefly the province of Bill France's NASCAR, but the USAC have also promoted the category since the club's inauguration in 1956. There were 19 races in the USAC's 1974 Stock Car Championship with purses ranging from $8150 to $67,785. Tracks ranged from half-mile dirt affairs to the full-blooded paved oval at Pocono. In recent years USAC Stock Car Division star has been Butch Hartman, the 35-year-old Ohio driver who sped himself to a record number of championships in four consecutive years from 1971 to 1974.

The USAC's 'shop window' is, of course, the USAC National Championship in general and the Indianapolis 500 in particular. The USAC are very jealous of their annual Indy 500 in May and over the years have been loathe to change the format. The race was in a rut when, in the early 1960s, the European influence was felt. Jim Clark and Graham Hill, British winners of the Indianapolis 500 in 1965 and 1966 respectively, had no intention of competing seriously in the USAC National Championship and promotors of races other than the Indianapolis 500 were upset they could not advertise the current Indy winner as a star attraction.

When the USAC was formed in 1956 the National Championship formula was set at 4500cc unsupercharged or 3000cc supercharged for racing engines or 5500cc for diesel motors. Turbine engines were encouraged with no limitations set. In practice, the four-cylinder Offenhauser engine reigned supreme with only the ultra-powerful, but unlucky, supercharged Novi V8s representing a challenge. Most cars were identical in layout, being of the so-called 'roadster'-type chassis —large, heavy, front-engined single-seaters equipped with rear-wheel-drive.

In 1957 a decision was made to try to reduce the speeds at Indianapolis. Engine sizes were cut to 4200cc unsupercharged and 2800cc supercharged, although the limit for diesels remained at 5500cc and the turbine category (for which there were no takers, yet . . .) continued unrestricted. This was also the year USAC went to Europe. The club was invited to send a team of Indianapolis-type machinery to race on the banked Monza track near Milan, Italy, against the fastest European cars. Of course, there was no equivalent European formula to the USAC National Championship's. In Grand Prix racing the limit was 2500cc unsupercharged, although there were in theory several sports car engines which could have been utilised in adapted Grand Prix chassis.

The idea, originated from Monza's director Giuseppe Bacciagaluppi, was warmly received by the USAC.

But it had a very different reception in Europe. The newly-formed *Union Pilotes Professionale International*, which represented Europe's Grand Prix drivers, decided to boycott the event, claiming that the banked Monza track was extremely dangerous, and that tyres would overheat, burst and precipitate accidents. It appeared as though the gaily-painted American machines would have the track to themselves until the Scottish Ecurie Ecosse team, winners of the previous week's Le Mans 24-hours, decided to enter three Jaguar D-type sports cars. Maserati entered two cars as Frenchman Jean Behra refused to participate in the UPPI boycott.

The 'Race of Two Worlds,' as the three-heat event was dubbed, was naturally dominated by USAC cars, Jimmy Bryan's Offenhauser-powered machine averaging over 160 mph and recording fastest lap of 54.1 s, 175.74 mph. No tyre failures were reported, although the retirement rate was high due to the bumpiness of the circuit. European honour was salvaged by the Jaguars which, displaying impressive reliability, finished fourth, fifth and sixth. Behra's Maseratis, a $3\frac{1}{2}$-litre V12-engined single-seater and a 4.2-litre sports machine both failed in practice.

The UPPI relented for the repeat in 1958. Ferrari entered two cars, a 4.2-litre V12 and a 2.9-litre V6, while Maserati ran a 4.2-litre V8 single-seater for Stirling Moss paid for by Eldorado ice cream. Ecurie Ecosse built a special Jaguar-powered, Lister-based single-seater in addition to entering two Jaguar D-types. A six-year-old Ferrari was handled by Franco-American Harry Schnell. In addition, the USAC arranged to make available two Indy-type machines for European drivers. One was entrusted to five-times World Champion Juan Manuel Fangio and the other to French veteran Maurice Trintignant. Fuel contract problems solved at the last minute, Fangio was beset with engine problems which kept him out of the first two of the three heats, and then his fuel pump failed. Trintignant, unable to understand instructions from the American owner of the car, was replaced by a young USAC driver named A. J. Foyt midway through the meeting. (Foyt was to become an Indianapolis legend, the most successful driver in USAC history.)

This time the Europeans put up a strong challenge, especially Luigi Musso in the 4.2 Ferrari who set best time in practice and battled for leadership until overcome by exhaust fumes from the American cars. Moss put up a brave fight in the ill-handling Eldorado Maserati until its steering failed on the banking and the car spun crazily, hitting the top retaining wall and demolishing three concrete posts before slithering to a halt. Moss was not hurt. The ultimate winner was Jim Rathmann, Jimmy Bryan took second place and the Ferrari shared by Phil Hill, Luigo Musso and Mike Hawthorn, third place.

It was an exciting race and one which augered well for a common racing formula for the United States and Europe. Sadly, this was not to be. The USAC continued unchanged, while in Europe the trend went to smaller and less-powerful cars. (USAC racing was also 'exported' in the mid-1960s, events being run in Japan, Argentina and Canada.)

USAC racing slumbered on, hardly noticing a European entry in the 1961 Indianapolis 500 which was to revolutionize the format of the National Championship car. Jack Brabham, the 1959 and 1960 World Champion, drove a 2.7-litre Coventry Climax-engined Cooper T54, a beefed up version of the firm's Formula One car. The only rear-engined machine in the race, it outhandled the traditional 4.2-litre Offy-engined 'roadsters', but was severely handicapped by lack of

power. Brabham drove steadily into ninth place.

In 1963 Dan Gurney, the American Formula One driver, introduced Ford to Colin Chapman of Lotus. The result was a small machine, the Lotus 29, powered by a powerful 4.2-litre Ford V8 engine. At first thought of as mere 'toys,' the Lotus-Fords demonstrated they were trend-setters and Jim Clark took a close second place to Parnelli Jones' oil-leaking 'roadster.'

Then the torrent began and people who had at one time tried to ban lightweight, rear-engined cars had to submit to progress. Indianapolis and USAC racing, awakened from its slumbers, came to the forefront of the international motor racing world once more. Leading racing car designers from throughout the world took up the challenge of building a potential Indy winner, while the rivalry between Offenhauser and Ford engines and drivers from Europe and America created

intense interest and packed in the crowds.

Possibly progress was too quick. Into the late 1960s it suddenly seemed that turbine power would oust the piston-engined cars almost overnight, a move which once again worried the USAC traditionalists. In 1955 and 1961 early attempts at building turbine-powered cars had been seen to fail. In 1966 another turbine entry failed to qualify for the Indianapolis 500, but the following year extrovert Andy Granatelli decided to build a turbine car to the existing regulations which limited the engines to a 22-sq in air inlet. It was an advanced chassis and the engine, a Pratt & Whitney ST6B-62 turbine built in Canada, sat alongside the driver, Parnelli Jones. The smoothly-delivered power was transmitted via four-wheel-drive transmission. Jones qualified on the second row of the grid and easily dominated the race until a gearbox bearing failed less

Above: Eppie Wietzes in action in his Lola T332 during a round of the 1974 North American Formula 5000 championship. The Canadian drove his privately entered car to several good places during the year and eventually finished fourth in the championship table

than 10 miles from the finish.

Granatelli was back in 1968 with a team of Pratt & Whitney-powered Lotus 56s which were raced by Graham Hill, Joe Leonard and Art Pollard. They failed again, but were moral winners. Carroll Shelby, too, entered turbine cars, although these were withdrawn before the race. Despite a reduction of inlet annulus from 22 to 16 sq in, the turbines seemed the cars of the future. But what future? The USAC successfully argued that turbines were too expensive and lacked spectacle and noise and could, in effect, kill USAC racing. The USAC Rules Committee proposed that turbines should be banned for 1969, but the USAC board (headed by retiring president Tom Binford) turned down the proposals. Instead, they reduced the turbine engines inlet annulus to 12 sq in, sufficient to make turbine propulsion totally uncompetitive. . . . In

addition, four-wheel-drive—the essential transmission for turbines—was to be banned from 1970 onwards. (From 1969 the capacity of turbocharged or supercharged engines was reduced from 2.8 to 2.66 litres and stockblocks increased from 5 to $5\frac{1}{4}$ litres.)

Andy Granatelli unsuccessfully challenged the USAC in the law-courts over the turbine question and later threatened steam- or Wankel-powered machinery, even women drivers, at Indianapolis. In 1969, however, Mario Andretti won the Indianapolis 500 in a Granatelli-entered Hawk-Ford and the two sides settled their differences.

Speeds continued to rise at Indianapolis. The next major drama was in 1973 when Art Pollard and Swede Savage were killed at the speedway and Salt Walther seriously injured. A move was made to reduce speed and reduce fuel capacity. Almost immediately after the race wing area was reduced by 9 sq in to 55 sq in and the allowable fuel to be consumed in a 500-mile race reduced by 35 gallons to 340, all of which had to be contained in a double-skinned 40-gallon fuel tank, necessitating several fuel stops. At the end of 1973 more restrictions were made: wings were trimmed further to 43, while the total amount of fuel to be carried was reduced again to 280 gallons.

The 1974 USAC National Championship Trail featured 14 races, highlighted by the three 500-milers at Indianapolis, Pocono and Ontario. Purses ranged from $50,150 to $1,015,686 for the Indianapolis 500 itself. Championship winner, with four wins and five seconds to his credit, was 40-year-old Bobby Unser from Albuquerque, New Mexico. Since 1956, the championship has gone to A. J. Foyt of Texas no fewer than five times (1960–64 and 1967): Foyt was also early leader of the 1975 series, unsettled at the time of writing. Mario Andretti won the title three times, while two-time winners have been Jimmy Bryan, Roger Ward, Joe Leonard and Bobby Unser.

Road racing is the antithesis of oval racing, yet the USAC has been involved with the sanctioning of road-racing since early in its career. In fact, in 1958 the USAC sanctioned professional sports car racing for the first time in the United States, in direct opposition to the Sports Car Club of America which refused to soil its hands with money. At the first race at Lime Rock in September 1958 many SCCA members lost their licences as they competed for the $500 first prize, which eventually went to George Constantine, driver of a 3.9-litre Aston Martin DBR2/390. The USAC also co-sanctioned a major international sports car race at Riverside in October. For the first time US oval-track competitors, US 'amateur' drivers and top European exponents raced against each other on equal terms.

For a time road-racing dropped from the curriculum of the USAC, apart from occasional sorties to tracks such as Mosport Park and Riverside with USAC National Championship cars. In 1974, however, an agreement was reached (not without politics) with the Sports Car Club of America to co-sanction the American Formula 5000 Championship. The rules were amended to permit USAC National Championship cars to participate alongside conventional Formula 5000 machinery, but apart from Bobby Unser's turbocharged Eagle-Offenhauser showing immense speed at Riverside at the end of the year the cars were not competitive.

For the future it does appear the United States Auto Club has a major role to play in international as well as American motor racing. Whether a common formula is ever devised which unites the different worlds of Formula One Grand Prix racing and USAC oval-track racing remains to be seen, however. MK

2437

MEASURING LESS THAN NOTHING

The fitting of a vacuum gauge can mean greater efficiency and economy and is always a valuable guide to detecting engine defects

WHEN THE PISTON of a 4-stroke engine travels downward on its induction stroke, it creates a partial vacuum in the inlet manifold. As the degree of vacuum developed in the manifold is directly related to engine efficiency, the condition of the engine and the way in which engine usage varies from the ideal can be shown on a gauge which measures the vacuum.

The degree of vacuum, or negative pressure, depends to a degree on the swiftness of the downward stroke (the engine speed) and partly on the amount of obstruction to the airflow caused by the throttle butterfly or valve. When running at a steady speed, there is a degree of vacuum which gives the most economic use of fuel: the engine draws in just a sufficient amount of air/fuel mixture to maintain speed.

To enable the vacuum to be measured, a gauge is connected by a flexible tube to the inlet manifold. The gauge, of the Bourdon tube type, registers from 0 in to 30 in (760 mm). It is useful to remember that atmospheric pressure (nil vacuum)=0 in and very high vacuum=30 in. To make readings easier, some gauges incorporate various coloured sectors on the scale and are commonly referred to as performance gauges. Often the sectors, and the basic information that can be obtained from them (assuming steady readings), are as follows.

Vacuum inches Hg	Sector Colour	Throttle Position	
0–5 (low vacuum)	Red	Open	Engine labouring or at high acceleration rate
5–10	Orange	Half open	Fast cruising or medium acceleration
10–18	Blue	Quarter open	Normal cruising, maximum fuel economy
18–21	Green	Closed	Engine idling. A steady reading indicates good engine condition.
21–30 (high vacuum)	Yellow	Closed	Engine overrunning, being used as brake

The inclusion of a vacuum gauge in the instrument array, besides assisting efficient and economical running, can be a valuable guide to various engine defects: for example, air leaks through the carburettor or inlet manifold gaskets will clearly reduce the vacuum (pointer moves towards zero), while a blocked inlet—usually the air cleaner—will increase it (pointer towards 30 in). Weak valve springs or worn valve guides will cause the

pointer to vibrate and many other defects, from compression leaks to carburettor maladjustment, can with experience, be determined by close attention to the behaviour of the gauge.

A few cars have a blanked-of threaded hole already provided for those wishing to fit a vacuum gauge, but usually the inlet manifold must be drilled and threaded close to the engine side of the carburettor. Since metal drillings will fall inside the manifold and could be drawn into the engine, it is strongly adivsed that the manifold be removed first. A union is then screwed into the hole.

The engine bulkhead must also be drilled, and the gauge fitted to a panel attached to the fascia. A flexible tube is then connected between the gauge and the manifold union. a grommet being fitted over the tube where it passes through the bulkhead.

For twin carburettors, the manufacturer's advice should be sought as to the correct point to drill the hole for the union. It should be noted that vacuum gauges are not normally suitable for the 3-cylinder, 2-stroke engines, nor for rear-mounted engines. AGH

Above: a vacuum gauge from Smiths Industries; not only does this give the vacuum in inches of mercury, but it gives an indication of fuel consumption

HAND-MADE AT ECONOMY PRICE

The Vale Special was a hand-made sports car sold at mass-production prices and was strictly for the sporting enthusiast

'THE VALE SPECIAL', wrote Grande Vitesse of *The Motor* in 1933, 'is a hand-made car with a low centre of gravity, handling well and possessing an ability to rev. Lively, it is a car for general use and has had successful competition experience.'

The car's manufacturers, the Vale Motor Company (London) Limited, of Portsdown Road, Maida Vale, London W9, described their product as 'The Hand-made Car at a Mass-Production Price', adding that it was 'built by enthusiasts for enthusiasts'.

The enthusiasts in question were three young men with a liking for fast cars: the Hon P. I. E. Pellow, R. O. Wilcoxen and R. A. Gaspar. The Vale was designed by 'Pow' Pellew (later the Earl of Exmouth): in its original incarnation it was powered by a modified 832 cc sidevalve Triumph engine, which was capable of propelling the diminutive car at 72 mph at 4750 rpm. Average fuel consumption was claimed to be 40 mpg, while the safe speeds in the intermediate gears were 20, 38 and 54 mph. Brakes were not unduly large, yet the Vale Special was said to be able to stop in 25 ft from 30 mph, a performance only bettered by the 4½-litre Invicta among its contemporaries.

Its usual form was as a two-seater, available as Standard Model A (£195) or De Luxe Model B (£220) though in 1933 a four-seater version, the Tourette was listed at £225.

It seems as though, despite a ground clearance of six inches, the little Vale was too low-slung to be of use as a trials car, while, conversely, its top speed was not enough to make it viable for sports-racing events. So, in 1934, its manufacturers took the unusual step of offering to re-engine existing cars with larger power units, Coventry Climax engines of either four cylinders and 1098 cc or six cylinders and 1476 cc. It was obvious, too, that those dreams of 'mass-production prices' had been over-ambitious, the cost was up to £310 for new cars with the four and £395 with the six. Also available was a 1242 cc ohc Meadows engine, known as the 12 hp four. A car with the latter power unit cost £365, though

Below: the light and nimble two-seater Vale Special; these were available in standard Model A form or the more luxurious de luxe Model B form. Only 103 models were built, however, and no more cars were built by the company after 1935

it's unlikely that more than one Meadows-engined Vale was actually delivered. This was known as the Adamson Special, and its 'hypertuned' Meadows 9/40 engine was reputedly 'specially built' and capable of propelling the car at 80 mph.

Fitted with an underslung chassis, and cellulosed black with chromium fittings, the Adamson Special lasted only a few months in the hands of its original owner before returning to the works to be resold. The depreciation that this car, among other Vales, suffered was truly horrifying: complete with a stock of racing spares, the Adamson was offered for only £140, a drop of well over 60 per cent in less than a year.

Nor did the touring cars fare much better: in October 1934 Sprosens Limited, of Great Portland Street, who appear to have been the nearest thing to a distributor that Vale ever had, were offering a brand new, unregistered, unblemished Vale Special De Luxe with full maker's guarantee at £180, a 42 per cent reduction on list price, while a second- secondhand 1934 two-seater de luxe was available at £150 and a 1933 two-seater at £125. But there was, it seems, great demand for these cars among the cognoscenti, despite their rapid fall in value; a trader named H. F. Edwards, also of Great Portland Street, offered 'Cash immediately for good Vales; any district'.

By this time, however, production of Vales had virtually ceased. The company's ambition all along had been to go into line-production with the car, but they were unable to raise sufficient capital to do this. Pow Pellow was forced to resign through ill-health, and Bang Wilcoxen (who later died at Dunkirk) was badly injured in a crash with a J3 MG Midget at Donington.

The three partners realised their assets and paid the outstanding bills; Allen Gaspar, who had been sales and competition manager, continued at the old address, now trading under the name Vale Engineering Company Limited, buying, selling and tuning sports cars, and building the odd Vale Special to order.

Vale Engineering seemed to specialise in GNs, both four- and two-cylinder models, holding a full stock of spares for these cyclecars, though once again they seemed to be undercharging for their wares: 'Dyson Special, specially built GN 750 cc 4-cylinder motor, built and tuned regardless of expense . . . £15'. Other gems from their 1935 stock included a Type 35 Bugatti (£110) and an underslung racing Amilcar (£40), not to mention a Grand Sport staggered two-seater Amilcar with 'Super-tuned motor' at £25!

Probably the last of the 103 Vale Specials built by this company was a supercharged racer built for Ian Connell in 1935. Fitted with a Centric blower driven by twin belts and operating at 4–5 psi boost, the Vale had a 1496 cc Coventry Climax engine, with overhead inlet and side exhaust valves.

Connell entered this car for the 500 mile 1935 race at Brooklands, but was forced to retire within the first hour with a cracked cylinder head. This overheating trouble was traced to the design of the radiator, which was subsequently modified. When it was running properly, Connell's Vale could record a maximum speed of 130 mph and was reportedly faster from a standing start than the contemporary ERA. Connell and Gaspar competed with this car at Donington and other venues such as the Brighton Speed Trials, but after 1936 Gaspar and his works manager, Bill Francis-James (formerly with Aston Martin and the Fox & Nicholl Talbot team) concentrated on the sales and tuning side of the business. No more Vale Specials were ever manufactured.   DBW

Above: probably the last Vale Special ever produced was this supercharged racer built in 1935 for Ian Connell; it was powered by a 1496 cc Coventry Climax engine fitted with a Centric blower driven by twin belts; Connell entered this car for the 1935 Brooklands 500 race, but was forced to retire during the early stages of the race. The car had a reputed top speed of 130 mph

KEEPING THE GASES IN CHECK

Over the years, automobile designers have experimented with many systems to open and close the valves

UNLESS IT IS VERY UNUSUAL, a four-stroke engine must have at least two valves to each cylinder. One, the inlet valve, must be large enough and open wide enough to admit a fresh charge of as much air and fuel as may be desired at the proper time; the other, the exhaust valve, must be able when opened to allow the egress of all the gases produced by combustion. When they are closed, these valves must seal their ports so as to be gas-tight despite the tremendous pressures reached in the combustion chamber after ignition. They must be able to withstand very high temperatures, attack by corrosive media, violent accelerations and shock loads, and brief spells of operation without lubrication; they must not get in the way of the piston, nor interfere with each other, must not consume much power to operate them, nor be expensive to make. They must not suffer deformation, nor get out of adjustment, nor move in any other way than as the designer intended, even though they may open and close at a cyclic rate of anything from a couple of hundred to several thousand times a minute, and even though the duration of opening may be of the order of one hundredth of a second; and they must be able to keep this up for hours on end, for months without attention and for years without replacement. It is a tall order.

It is amazing that the things work at all, and it is not at all surprising that there have been hundreds of attempts to substitute some other kind of mechanism to perform their tasks. In the context of the motor car, such variants are most unusual, and they appear to have as little chance in the future as in the past of coming into favour, however great their theoretical or practical advantages. In automobile engineering, as in most other kinds, the first successful solution to a problem tends to be adopted so widely that any later ones, however much better, are excluded by the costs of revised tooling, by factory methods, and by deeply ingrained ways of thinking. So, by an accident of history, we still accept today the poppet valve that was the first to be effective when the four-stroke engine was applied to the propulsion of the earliest cars. It is a dreadful device that has been derided as a 'penny on a stick': the disc portion has a conical edge corresponding to that of the orifice it should seal, while the stem passes through and is supported by a cylindrical bearing or guide and is subjected to a never ending conflict of axial loads, from the springs pulling the valve down towards its seat and the operating mechanism that intermittently pushes it in the opposite direction. As with most engine components, the design of the valve is full of compromises: a head shape that is good for mechanical strength may be bad for temperature distribution, one that is good for efficient gas flow at maximum lift may cause unnecessary obstruction of the port when it is only partially open, while the subtleties of seat angling and radiusing (which have a profound effect on gas flow) may be confounded by the proximity of cylinder walls or piston crowns.

Only a few engineers and the best of mechanics worry about these things. Only they concern themselves with such niceties as the relationship between the width of the exhaust-valve seat (which, it used to be thought, had to be fairly wide in order to provide an escape path for the heat of the valve) and the valve-seat pressure, the truth of the matter being that the narrower the seat the greater is the pressure and the better the heat flow; only they accept the importance of really precise contouring of the edges of the valve and of its seat, knowing that these can have so great an influence on the coefficient of discharge of the valve as to be worth a 30% increase in valve lift. Everybody else is much more concerned with the location and size of the valves, and most particularly with the means of opening them.

Without exception among the four-stroke engines in production, the valve is lifted from its seat by a cam —an eccentric device which, as it rotates, displaces the valve either directly or indirectly, and then allows it to be returned to its seat with further rotation, the work of returning the valve being done almost invariably by some kind of springs. The cam appears to be not only eccentric but also brutal, and many have been the efforts to substitute something else: there have been obscure engines in which the work has been done by complicated linkages driven by the crankshaft, all straps and stirrups and sliding pins in sloppy slots; but by a nice philological paradox, all these may now be considered more eccentric than the cam itself.

Even the cam has taken many forms: there have been engines with face cams, conical cams, internal or ring cams and numerous other varieties, but today the cam is always a simple lobed eccentric integral with a shaft driven at half the crankshaft speed by any convenient and positive means. Its shape, which determines the

Top: a very simple valve arrangement used in the Salmson of 1922; in this, one pushrod was used to open the inlet and exhaust valves alternately by means of a centrally pivoted rocker arm; not, of course, the most efficient system

Above: probably the most popular valve mechanism for many years; the valves are mounted in line in the head and are opened by a block-mounted camshaft via pushrods and rockers, and closed by strong springs; adjustment of the tappet clearance is by means of lock-nutted screws fitted to the rockers

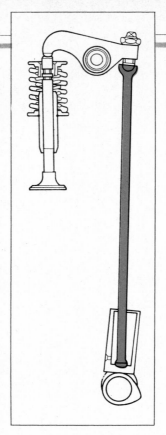

Right: the components of the 'standard' pushrod-and-rocker set-up; the camshaft is mounted in the crankcase or cylinder block, while the valves are mounted in the cylinder head

Below right: the Itala rotary-valve system, introduced in their 25 hp model of 1912 and kept in production until 1922, when it was still fitted to the type 55 six-cylinder engine

timing of opening and closure of the valve and also its rates of ascent and descent, is compounded of many subtleties but whilst its shape is often the work of very clever men, they are even cleverer who design the valve springs which play a dominant part in the whole proceedings. It is the spring that determines how rapidly the valve may be lifted by the cam, how faithfully it will follow the cam's dictates in descending again and how precisely and positively it will be returned to its seat and kept there until it is next due to open. Not only the mass of the valve, but also that of all the other components in the valve train between valve and cam, must be controlled and shifted by the spring; and this includes an assortment of cotters, rockers, pushrods, tappets, adjusters and oil seals. The most popular kind of springs is helical, concentric with the valve stem and often abetted by another of smaller diameter and different rate fitting fairly closely within it; but it was at one time thought preferable that really high-performance engines should have springs of the so-called hairpin type, which took up a lot of space laterally, but little vertically (so the valve stems could be shorter and therefore lighter) and which could run at very high frequencies without encountering the resonance problems commonly affecting helical springs. In fact, both kinds of springs, helical and hairpin alike, are merely compact and complex versions of the torsion bar, and spring technology has come far

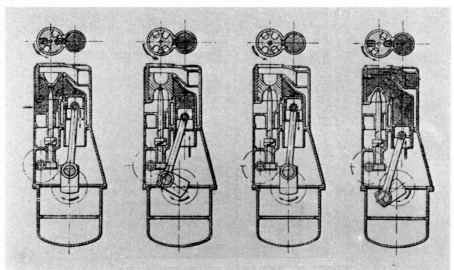

Right: eight examples of different valve arrangements, all of which have been popular at some time for reasons either of high efficiency or for their low cost

Below: with a rocker it is possible to enlarge or decrease the lift of the valve relative to that of the camshaft; if a and b are the lengths of the two parts of the rocker, and the camshaft lift is represented by A, then the valve list is A × a/b; with direct-acting cams, the valve lift is equal to the camshaft lift

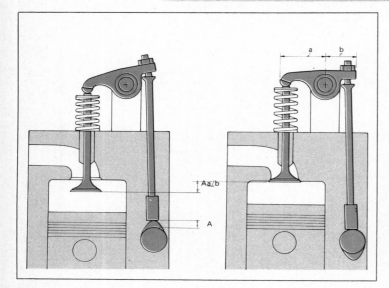

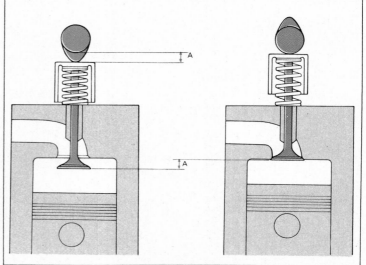

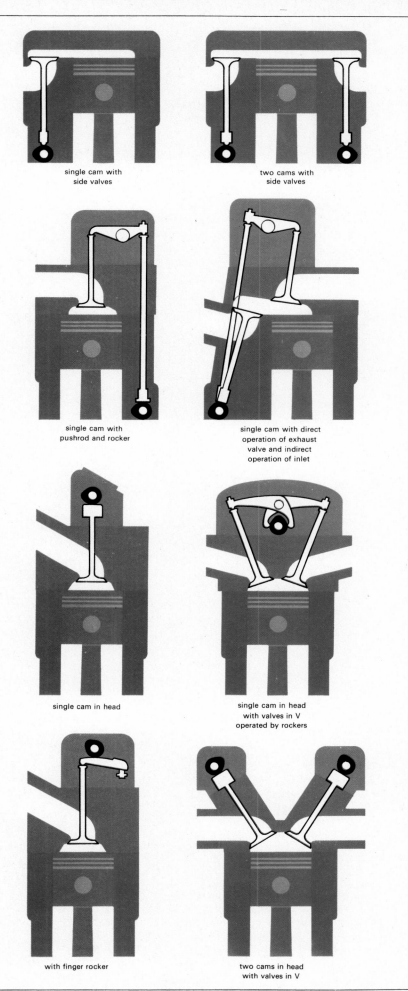

single cam with
side valves

two cams with
side valves

single cam with
pushrod and rocker

single cam with direct
operation of exhaust
valve and indirect
operation of inlet

single cam in head

single cam in head
with valves in V
operated by rockers

with finger rocker

two cams in head
with valves in V

enough now for it to be possible to make helical springs that will not pass through natural resonance frequencies anywhere in the operating range of the engine. The means whereby it is done are numerous. For a start, the number of coils is minimised, although it should never be less than four and a half) so as to reduce the mass and inertia of the spring; and progressive-rate springs are now popular, a progressively decreasing pitch on the coils having the result of varying the number of effective coils throughout the lifting and lowering operation (as they are in turn compressed solid, starting from the closest pitched end), the natural frequency of the spring varying accordingly, and surge being thus avoided, possibly at some cost in noise of operation which can be heard as a hiss. There are still some vehicles around in which the springs are true simple straight torsion bars, although the last cars to employ these were, in production, the Panhard flat twins, and in racing the Formula Two Honda engine used in the Brabham chassis in 1966.

In the primeval days of the petrol engine when speeds were low, when gas inertia was ignored and when big stationary industrial engines provided what little guidance was available, only the exhaust valves would be mechanically opened and subsequently controlled by a rotating cam. The inlet valve was left to its own devices, and was supposed to function automatically. It was made very light and held on its seat by an extremely light spring: when the piston had descended sufficiently on its suction stroke to reduce the pressure within the cylinder below that of the ambient atmosphere, the pressure difference would force the valve open against its feeble spring, which would close it again as soon as parity of pressures was almost achieved. If the spring were too heavy the valve would not open for long enough, but if it were too light the valve might not be properly sealed when closed, and it could not move sufficiently quickly. When mechanical operation of the inlet valve was popularised by Maybach in the 1901 Mercédès, the stage was set for rapid improvement in engine performance.

From then on, it became common, albeit briefly, for an in-line multi-cylinder engine to have two camshafts. Today, one of the first questions of an enthusiast about a new engine is an enquiry about how many camshafts it has and where they might be; but in those days they were always set in the flanks of the crankcase where they could conveniently be driven by half-speed gearing from the nose of the crankshaft. The camshaft on one side would operate the inlet valves, that on the other the exhaust valves, and the resulting configuration of side valves was popularly described as the T-Head. It allowed the manufacture of nice symmetrical castings that did not suffer too much from distortion, and it allowed plenty of room for access to the valves, usually through threaded plugs in the top of the shallow cylinder head; but it made it quite impossible to contrive a compact well shaped combustion chamber, and the studies carried out by Ricardo encouraged most manufacturers to adopt side-by-side valves in what was distinguished as the L-head configuration: it had the added virtue of manufacturing economy, since all the necessary cams could be made integral with a single shaft, reducing the number of bearings and gears in the engine, although making the casting of the cylinder block rather more difficult since inlet and exhaust passages now had to enter and leave it on the same side.

In modest cars for the man in the street, L-head engines survived for decades, especially in the USA and Great Britain. Difficulties of aspiration through the necessarily tortuous passages, of combustion control, and of compression ratio, prevented it from ever being very powerful; but those same breathing difficulties, which became more and more pronounced as the speed rose, gave it a most welcome back-up torque characteristic, so that the 'sidevalver' became renowned for its flexibility. This was an engine characteristic in great demand before the days of the synchromesh gearbox: the Americans tended to have fairly big engines and did not need to change gear much, the English to have fairly small ones, but all too often they could not change gear much, so in either case the side-valve unit was popular until the early 1950s. From the valve-gear point of view, it was attractive in some ways, for the camshaft could

ness of gas flow into and out of it; and no designer conscious of new things can long reconcile himself to a side-valve layout. From that time on, half the developments in valve gear (an unfortunate term, but *valve mechanism* evidently took too long to say for it to become a popular expression) were merely means to a different end, which was securing good combustion-chamber shape and port shapes; the rest have merely been contrivances to allow the valves to be put where they were wanted without vast manufacturing expense or forbidding maintenance difficulties.

Because there is more to engine design than simply making the valves big and moving them easily, the

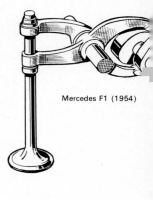

Mercedes F1 (1954)

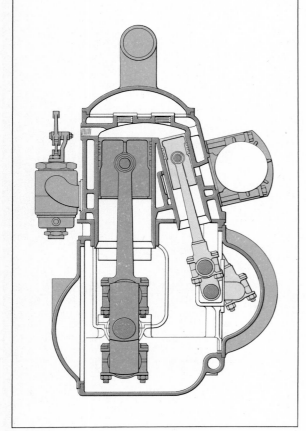

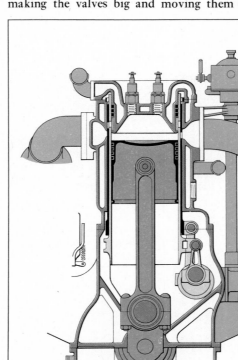

Duca (195

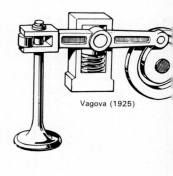

Vagova (1925)

exercise almost direct attack upon the valve stems with no interposition needed except of simple light cylindrical tappets to take the side thrust from the wiping action of the cams, rather than allow the slender and ill-supported valve stems to suffer it. Thus, the valve train weight was as little as it could be; and with the entire apparatus lodged in the crankcase and cylinder block—which were generally integrated—there were very few problems of differential expansion, and so adjustment of the slight clearances necessary between tappets and cams or valve stems was not too often needed. When it had to be done, it could be done easily, for the mechanism was readily accessible—or at least it was until more voluminous bodywork came into vogue, whereupon it began to be very difficult indeed to reach the valve chest.

Long before this unhappy situation came about, particular people had tired of the inefficiency that was the root cause of the 'sidevalver's' flexibility. Studies of the combustion process, in which once again Ricardo was outstanding but by no means the first, and perhaps only by a short head the greatest, had begun to dominate engine-design thinking, as had some aware-

half-way house known as ohiv (overhead inlet valve, the exhaust valve remaining in the original side-valve position) was doomed from the start. It allowed the valves to be very large, admittedly; but the exhaust valve was still badly located for cooling, while the inlet valve (which was large and heavy to start with) had entrained with it a pushrod and rocker to communicate motion from the camshaft—still tucked away in the bowels of the engine—and so the advantages were not very great, while the disadvantages of a singularly clumsy combustion-chamber shape remained to make such engines unsuitable for all but a certain class of Rover and Rolls-Royce customer. The properly efficient overhead-valve engine had both sets of valves overhead—but the production engineers were still wedded to their old crankcases with a place for the camshaft within, where it could be driven by the simplest of means (usually gears or a chain) from the nose of the crankshaft, and where it could conveniently serve also to drive the oil pump and ignition distributor by means of a skew gear conventionally set at or near its middle. With the camshaft down here, and the valves up there, communication promised to be difficult.

Above, far left: the Hewitt valve arrangement of 1905, with an auxiliary piston to control the flow of inlet charge and exhaust gas

Above left: the Knight double sleeve-valve layout, in which the two sleeves slide up and down under the command of a special crankshaft

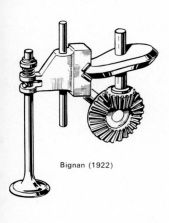

Bignan (1922)

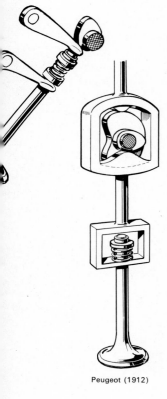

Peugeot (1912)

Above: a selection of desmodromic valves employed over the years; different manufacturers have their own ways of causing positive closing of the valves

Right: the Aspin rotary valve is one of the few alternatives to the poppet valve which has been taken seriously as an efficient competitor

A conventional solution was to employ pushrods and rockers. Tappets or cam followers still took the brunt of the cam lobes' attack, transferring the lateral loads through their cylindrical faces to the bores in which they moved piston-like in the crankcase casting. Hemispherical recesses on the upper face of the tappets accepted ball-ended rods, sometimes solid and slender, at other times tubular and stiff, reaching up to higher altitudes than the valves themselves, and prodding rocker beams whose other extremities levered down the valves against the usual springs. It all meant a lot of extra weight, and so the springs had to be stronger, which in turn meant higher seating pressures, and higher loads throughout the valve-actuating mechanism. The fact that engines of this type run to higher speeds than the old 'sidevalvers' commonly did was due to the better breathing and burning that the arrangement made possible, for mechanically the system was basically *less* suited to high-frequency operation. This in itself forced engineers to exercise a good deal more brainpower on the evolution of improved cam shapes, with the result that there have been some pushrod engines capable of running very fast indeed: 10,000 rpm in Formula Three engines a few years ago, and even higher figures in motor cycles earlier still (how about 11,000 rpm in the 'works' 350 Douglas of the early 1950s?) indicate that such systems can be made to work well.

Apart from getting the cam right and the springs reliable, most of the difficulties centred around adjustment and variation of the necessary back-lash in the system. Different expansion rates of all the various components as they grew hot during operation would cause the overall length of the operating train to vary considerably. The back-lash had to be kept as small as possible, not only to reduce the noise, but also to minimise the mechanical shock of impact as clearances were taken up during the valve-lifting phase; but if the clearances were too small, there would be a danger that when everything reached a certain temperature, the clearances would disappear altogether, and the valve might not be free to seat properly, in which case it would quickly be wrecked by flames searing through the gap.

The first and last palliative to be effective was the hydraulic or zero-lash tappet, essentially a small piston inside a larger one, with the intervening space being taken up by high-pressure oil, the pressure being sufficient to ensure that all the usual clearances were taken up at all times, but at the same time not high enough to be capable of lifting the valve off its seat. Ordinary engine oil from the delivery side of the pump was led into the tappets and bled out of them again, and the result was an ohv engine that could be remarkably quiet mechanically. The hydraulic tappet has become almost the norm in the engines of luxury cars and most big Americans, but not without introducing a few snags of its own: the two most notable are, first, a critical tendency to internal corrosion (making hydraulic tappets the most demanding part of a modern engine from the oil technologists' viewpoint) and an inability to operate accurately at very high speeds, which is why zero-lash tappets do not figure in high-performance engines.

Many other refinements were introduced to ohv operation by pushrods. In an effort to reduce the mass of the operating mechanism, camshafts were sometimes set very high in the cylinder block, so that the pushrods could be made correspondingly shorter and stiffer. Some manufacturers, including Riley, Lea-Francis, and Darracq, went one better by having exhaust and inlet camshafts mounted high on opposite

flanks of the cylinder block, thus making it possible for the inlet and exhaust valves to be placed opposite each other and inclined into a hemispherical combustion chamber, rather than being condemned to stand in line along the length of the cylinder head, to the detriment of breathing and combustion-chamber shape alike. Other manufacturers tried cheaper ways of achieving the same valve arrangement, sometimes by grotesquely long rockers reaching across the head from one side to the other, sometimes by transverse pushrods transmitting motion from primary rockers at the top of the vertical pushrods to secondary ones in contact with the valves on the far side of the head.

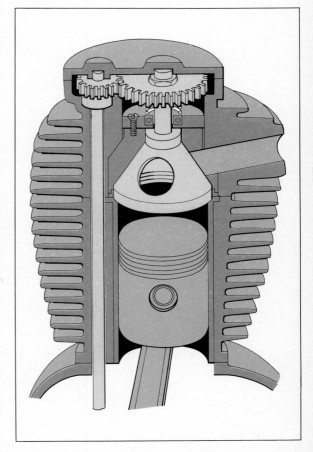

It may seem extraordinary that they should go to such lengths when the logical thing to do, having transposed the valves to their desired positions in the cylinder head, would have been to shift the camshaft or shafts up there too, so as to provide direct attack without all the intermediary burden of pushrods and rockers. In racing, of course, this step was taken early, a sharp Swiss called Ernest Henry stealing the idea from his employer, Marc Birkigt (another Swiss, but cleverer and better behaved) at Hispano-Suiza and taking it to Peugeot for exploitation in their racing cars in the second decade of this century. This arrangement it should be emphasised, was of two overhead camshafts, separately controlling banks of inlet and exhaust valves that could therefore be disposed freely according to the designer's preferences concerning porting and combustion-chamber design; a single overhead camshaft operating in-line valves or, in more developed form, operating inclined opposing valves by means of rockers, had been used by Fiat and Mercédès years earlier.

In racing, and in the best-bred sports cars, overhead camshafts were considered *de rigueur* by the 1920s; in luxury cars, touring cars and especially the cheaper types that were built up in large quantities and down to a price, they were considered untenable by production engineers and salesmen for very much longer. Their objections were wholly practical rather than theoretical, being based mainly on the difficulty of providing a suitable drive from the crankshaft to the camshafts without indulging in expansion joints and expensive gears that were in any case likely to be noisy. Eventually some engineers made tentative experiments with

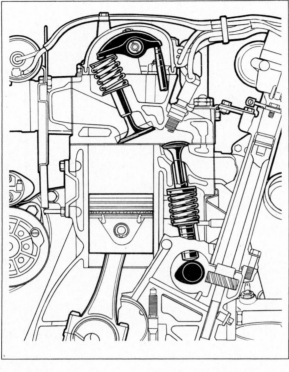

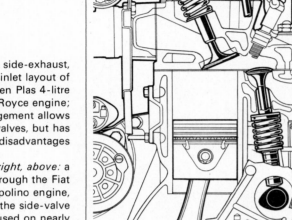

Right: the side-exhaust, overhead-inlet layout of the Vanden Plas 4-litre R's Rolls-Royce engine; this arrangement allows for big valves, but has several disadvantages

Far right, above: a section through the Fiat Topolino engine, showing the side-valve set-up used on nearly every car in the early days of motoring; although simple to operate, the side valve limits combustion-chamber design

Far right, below: the pushrod-and-rocker arrangement is simple, allowing overhead valves and block-mounted cam, but the mass of the linkage tends to limit the speed of operation; this diagram is of a Fiat 124 engine

chains, notably Weller who designed the two-litre AC and invented a spring-bladed chain tensioner that would do a fairly satisfactory job of taking up any slack in the drive. Noise remained a problem because it was more difficult to damp the clatter of valve gear at the top of an engine than in its bottom, and chains were often of parlous durability; moreover, the difficulties of adjusting tappet clearances gave the overhead camshaft a very bad name among mechanics in the trade, who did not take kindly to having to strip most of the mechanism in order to insert shims between the valve stem tips and the conventional piston-type tappets.

Not until the late 1960s were these difficulties overcome, when Fiat and General Motors both made notable contributions to the state of the art and allowed overhead-camshaft engines to be enjoyed by the most ordinary and unambitious of motorists. The problem of providing a satisfactory drive was dealt with by the newly developed internally toothed belt, which was quieter, more positive, more easily tensioned and much more easily installed than the chain. The rest of the noise problem was dealt with at source by refinements of cam profile, designed to take up back-lash gradually, rather than suddenly. As for lash adjustment, the best modern means is probably that which was adapted by Fiat from an earlier design by the engineer Remor for MV Agusta racing motor cycles, and employed first by Fiat in the engine of their 125 car. Here, the adjusting shims fit into a recess on top of the inverted cup tappet so that adjustment is merely a matter of using a special tool to compress the

spring and hold the tappet down, while the appropriate shim can be slipped between tappet and cam. The General Motors method, first seen in the Vauxhall Victor at about the same time, was undoubtedly ingenious: a fine-threaded hole is bored at an angle of $5\frac{1}{2}°$ into the tappet and a taper-faced adjusting screw is wound into it. The taper on the screw corresponds to the angle of the hole, so the face is at right-angles to the axis of the tappet and provides an abutment for the tip of the valve stem. Each turn of the screw alters the

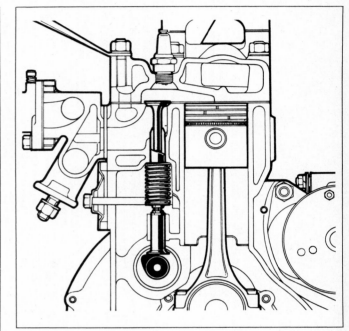

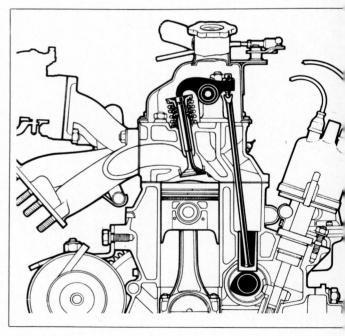

clearance by 0.003 inch. Unfortunately, the Vauxhall system makes the tappet itself rather heavy, putting reciprocating weight where it is not wanted, and thus negating a basic advantage of overhead-camshaft location. Thus, for a valve weighing 3.23 oz, the Vauxhall valve train's sprung mass amounted to 7.734 oz, of which 3.74 were accounted for by the tappet; by contrast, Fiat's corresponding inlet valve, weighing 3.315 oz, was part of a sprung valve-train mass totalling

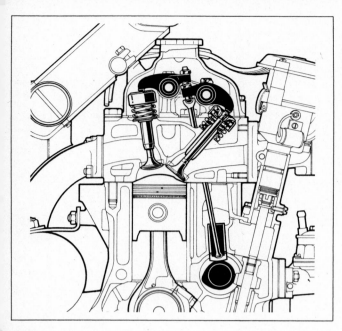

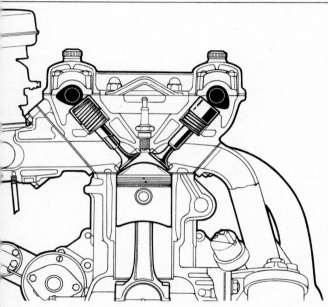

only 6.911 oz, the tappet accounting for 1.834 oz.

Those manufacturers preferring to interpose rockers or finger followers between a cam and the valve stem sometimes provide the necessary adjustment by pivoting the fingers on individual ball studs which can be screwed up or down to vary their height. In the most refined versions of this system, the pillar supporting the rocker or lever pivot is pumped up by engine oil pressure to maintain zero back-lash, on principles exactly similar to those of the hydraulic tappet.

Given all these refinements, the single overhead camshaft is very efficient, and the advantage of shaft duplication are more difficult to justify. The main one is that it leaves the space between the banks of valves clear for the insertion of spark plugs or downdraught inlet ports, or coolant conduits, as well as giving the designer complete freedom to choose whatever included angle he likes between the two banks of valves. This angle is in turn determined by his preferences in combustion-chamber and port design but, in any case, the convention of two inclined valves in a hemi-spherical combustion chamber, as introduced by Fiat

in 1921 and emulated by all the best racing and sporting engines up to the 1960s, received a rude shock when Honda began to produce racing motor cycles with very small cylinders in which nevertheless they found it worthwhile to set four valves, however tiny. Honda had the advantage of being a young firm un-fettered by tradition, so it was mere coincidence that this four-valve layout should constitute a reversion to the Edwardian practice instigated by Birkigt with the Hispano-Suizas.

A multiplicity of small valves is a good thing. It allows an engine to run hotter, for a small valve has a greater ratio of surface area to mass than has one that is larger but geometrically similar; thus, the small valve

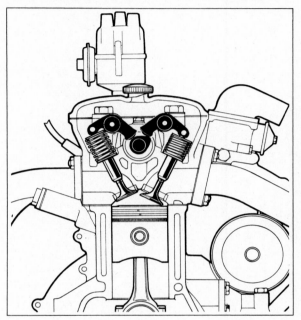

is better able to shed heat. It allows higher rates of revolution, for a small valve has less mass for the cams to accelerate and the springs to control. It allows high volumetric efficiency, for the area of the four biggest valves that can be squeezed into a given head is greater than that of the two biggest valves that can there be placed, and the engine's port areas will be commen-surately greater.

The same ends could be achieved by the use of desmodromic valve gear, in which positive mechanical closure of the valves supplants springs and allows longer and higher valve lift. Daimler-Benz did it with complete success in their Grand Prix cars of 1954 and 1955, while Ducati swept their motor-cycling board with it even earlier, and for that matter there were successful four-wheeled exemplars as early as the Grand Prix Delage of 1914. However, it requires a greater degree of engineering skill to make satisfactory desmodromic valve gear than it does to insert half-sized valves in double the numbers into an engine, and so the example of Honda was soon followed by others. In 1962, the V6 GP Ferrari was modified to have 24 valves instead of twelve, a change that allowed the power output and the engine speed both to be raised by about 5%. Three years later, the Coventry Climax V8 GP engine was introduced in 32-valve form, the reduced inertia of the lighter valves making possible an rpm increase of 12%. This was accompanied by improvements in power and torque of 5% and 3% respectively, while the four-valved engine also had a useful power band of 3500 rpm, 1000 more than the range of the two-valve unit. Moreover, the increase in

Left: an ingenious arrangement used by BMW in their 1800 to operate two inclined valves per cylinder with one overhead camshaft; the inclined valves make possible a hemispherical or pent-roofed combustion chamber, either of which is efficient

Far left, above: another way of operating inclined valves with one camshaft; this Fiat 1800 engine has its pushrods in line, driving through opposed pushrods

Far left, below: one of the most popular layouts of the 1960s and 70s is this one, with inclined overhead valves operated directly by a pair of camshafts; this keeps the mass of the mechanism as low as possible; the engine shown is that of the Alfa Romeo Giulia

Above: four types of valve-operating rocker which have been used at various times in the history of motoring

Right: two ways of operating inclined valves; with one cam and rockers, or with two cams

low fuel consumption (not to mention its ability to use very low-grade fuel) due to its automatic charge stratification. At the time of writing, the Aspin and the Cross were both still being earnestly developed and propounded, which was more than could be said for the various kinds of sleeve valve which also attracted engineers in the past. In fact, the sleeve valve is the only type that has rivalled the poppet valve for any significant period in the history of the motor car: the Knight double-sleeve valve was extensively used by Daimler, Minerva, Willys and (especially throughout the best part of the two decades between the World Wars) by Panhard; the Burt single-sleeve valve was employed by Argyll in 1912 and by Vauxhall in 1926, thereafter being taken up by Bristol, and later Napier,

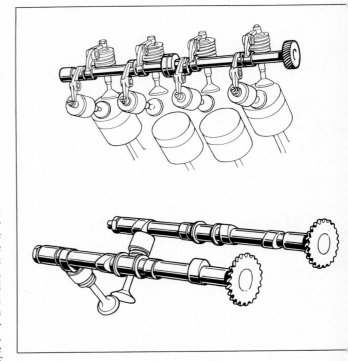

maximum speed being greater than the increase in power, it was possible for gear ratios in a given installation to be lowered, thus multiplying the engine torque so that there was even more surplus tractive effort available at the driving wheels for acceleration from a given speed. Honda having demonstrated in a technical paper some years ago that the pentroof head of the four-valve engine is as good as the hemispherical head of the two-valve type in terms of combustion efficiency (and, incidentally, that the two are appreciably better than any other popular configuration), the speed advantage remains clear, together with the possibility that the smaller valves may be made of a cheaper material because the smaller size means they are inherently cooler running.

Of course, there have been designers and inventors galore to whom the whole idea of the reciprocating poppet valve and all its attendant mechanism was anathema. History records a plethora of rotary valves, piston valves, sleeve valves and numerous others, all apparently intended to substitute nice continuous motions for the nasty accelerations and decelerations to which the poppet is doomed; but they themselves were doomed to failure, simply because the earliest of them came just a few years too late, and because during the critical period of their development, metallurgy was some years ahead of lubrication, which was usually their Achilles heel. Today, poppet valves can be made to function as fast as may be desired, but the best rotary valves have other advantages that may still validly be championed. These include the elimination of hot spots in the combustion chamber, the reduction of operating noise, very fast opening of the ports (important when exploiting gas dynamics for good charging and scavenging), completely clear throughways at maximum port opening, and often a better shape for the combustion chamber. Undoubtedly, the best and most promising are the Cross and the Aspin, the former having been developed to a greater immunity from lubrication problems and the latter showing itself particularly good at combining high power with a very

in some of the most outstanding aviation engines ever to leave planet Earth—or at least ever to make it off the ground with pistons.

The principle of the sleeve valve is that of a loose liner forming the cylinder bore and which is free to move in a required path, its outer surface fitting closely in the fixed bore of the cylinder block, and constituting a bearing, while holes in the sleeve register at appropriate times with fixed ports in the block. With a simple linear motion along the axis of the bore, a single sleeve cannot give satisfactory port timing, but if two concentric reciprocating sleeves are moved out of phase, perfectly satisfactory timing can be attained, and this was the basis of the Knight system. For a single sleeve, the necessary motion is partly axial and partly rotational, the result being a continuous elliptical movement, and this was the outcome of Burt's ideas. It demands very high-quality manufacture, and rather expensive materials, if it is to work satisfactorily, but there are no other objections to it, and it undoubtedly gives exceptional results. It may be worth pointing out that the sleeve-valve Napier Sabre had the highest specific power output of any piston engine in aviation, while the sleeve-valved Bristol Centaurus was, in its final civil form, the most reliable, having an overhaul life of no less than three thousand hours, which is equivalent to about five years driving by the average motor-car user.   LJKS

CHOOSING THE RIGHT MOMENT

Without correct valve timing the engine is likely to perform like a symphony orchestra without a conductor

WHEN WE ARE FIRST introduced to the four-stroke cycle, we are taught that the four successive motions of the piston, taking place during two consecutive revolutions of the crankshaft, correspond to the induction, compression, combustion and exhaust phases. Like so many other simplifications drilled into us in the elementary stages of our education and upbringing, this is simply inaccurate and untrue. An engine in which the inlet valve opened with the piston at the top of its stroke, and closed again when it reached the bottom to complete the supposed induction phase, followed after an interval of 360° crankshaft rotation by the exhaust valve opening with the piston at the bottom of its stroke, and closing when it had reached the top, would admittedly work—but it would only work very slowly. Its combustion would be dirty, its power slight and its usefulness as an automotive propulsion unit seriously debatable. It takes time to set a column of air in motion, and once this has been done it will keep on keeping on for some time after the inductive encouragement has been suspended, for there is inertia in air as in anything

engineering. As the power is increased, so flexibility diminishes: the engine with long valve openings and overlap will not run slowly, just as the engine with elementary timing will not run fast.

The modern petrol engine is essentially a high-speed engine, its maximum cyclic frequency rising steadily with the passage of the years. Touring-car engines

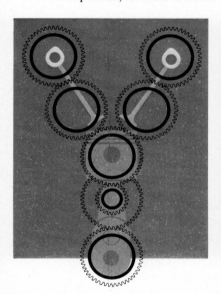
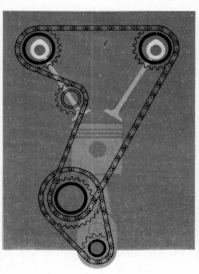
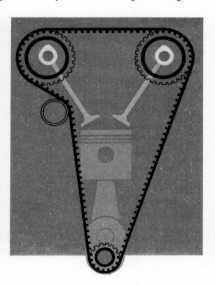
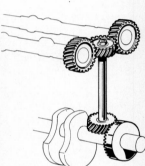

Above and left: four ways of driving overhead camshafts from the crankshaft—from left these are with gears, chain, internally toothed belt and shaft; the toothed belt is a recent innovation and it has two advantages in that it is quiet and it runs outside the engine, needing no lubrication

else having mass. The same applies to the waste gases produced by combustion, and the lesson to be deduced from all this is that if the engine is to be efficient as a pump—which in some senses is what it amounts to—the valves must be opened before basic logic suggests it should be necessary, and their closure should be deferred until some time later than might be thought prudent. In fact, during the 720° of crankshaft rotation involved in a complete four-stroke cycle, the inlet valve of even the most mild-mannered modern touring car will be open for about 230°, the exhaust valve will be open for about the same extent and there will be a brief period of perhaps 25° overlap during which the exhaust valve will not yet have shut, and the inlet valve will already have opened. That leaves only 285° for the compression and expansion phases that theoretically occupy 360°. When one looks at the valve timing of a racing engine, one is faced with the paradox that, despite the reduction of this period (when the useful work might be supposed to be done) to something like 190°, the power output is very much greater. Clearly it is the time (or rather, the proportion of the time) spent in pumping gases in and out of the engine that varies more or less in proportion to the power achieved: in a Grand Prix engine, each valve may be open for about 325°, both open and overlapping for as much as 120°.

Of course, there are attendant disadvantages, compromise raising its ugly head here as elsewhere in

currently turn over at rates of rpm that were considered the giddy limit for sports-car engines twenty years ago, and were the exclusive preserve of racers twenty years before that. About ten years ago, there were racing motor cycles with four-stroke engines reaching 23,000 rpm, and their manufacturer (Honda) subsequently asserted in a technical paper that most of the problems of petrol engine operation disappear beyond 10,000 rpm! Even without going to such extremes—if they are extremes, for research was already being carried out then on engines whose pistons fluttered up and down 50,000 times a minute—the kinetic energy of a moving mass of gas can be exploited in surprising ways.

If the exhaust be opened some time before the piston has completed its expansion stroke, the pressure of combustion gases in the cylinder will be so high that they will rush out precipitately through the exhaust port when it opens, departing with such violence and velocity that they leave a partial vacuum behind them in the cylinder. If the inlet valve is then opened sufficiently early that low pressures will immediately induce a flow of fresh charge air into the cylinder through the inlet port, despite the fact that the piston is still rising towards the top of its stroke, and might be thought to be compressing the cylinder's contents. In fact, during the overlap period, while both valves are open, the rarefaction left in the exhaust ports by the headlong departure of the exhaust gases communicates such a strong suction effect to the inlet port that volumes of fresh air are drawn straight though to the combustion chamber, cooling it and scouring out the last traces of vitiated gases, so that when the exhaust valve closes, with the piston already on its way down the cylinder, the column of air in the inlet tract has been so energetically accelerated that it will keep on piling into the cylinder even after the piston has reached the bottom of its stroke and has started moving upwards again. Clearly the art—or science—lies in knowing when each valve should open and close.

In the case of engines developing very high bhp per unit of capacity, the operating characteristics of the valves themselves become of major importance. In endeavouring to obtain acceleration and opening periods aimed at a certain specific power output, many forms of cam contour have appeared, but since any alteration in this respect must affect the whole of the operating gear in important matters such as power loss, noise, reliability and maintenance of tune, it is obvious that any departure from established practice has to be thoroughly tested. Ideally, each valve should reach its full lift instantaneously, remain fully open for the whole of this period and close in the same manner as it opened. In practice, the limiting factors in obtaining the maximum through-way area for the longest period are three: the rate of acceleration that the valve train can sustain, the rate of deceleration that the valve springs can ensure and the maximum velocity that the valve may be permitted to attain.

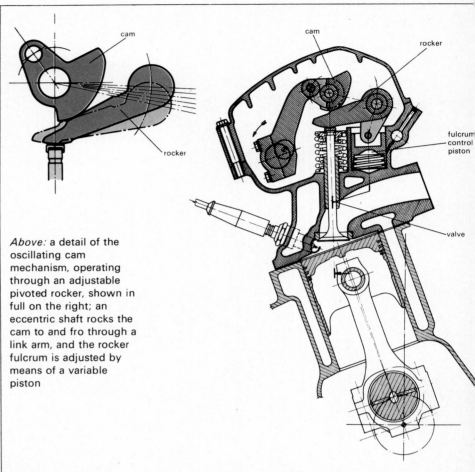

Above: a detail of the oscillating cam mechanism, operating through an adjustable pivoted rocker, shown in full on the right; an eccentric shaft rocks the cam to and fro through a link arm, and the rocker fulcrum is adjusted by means of a variable piston

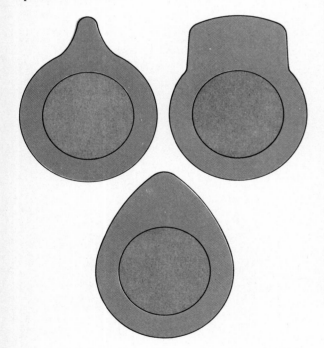

These factors unfortunately turn most discussions of cam profiles into cumbersome and scarcely intelligible displays of advanced mathematics. Essential as it may be to the practitioner, an understanding of such mathematics is not necessary to the discussion of the principles involved. In avoiding the maths, we will instead have to consider a few practical facts—practical because, although the problems they create can be circumvented by elaborate means such as the use of desmodromic valve mechanisms, such means are generally considered too expensive to be justified.

Valve float is the first of these uncomfortable facts. For a valve of given mass and subject to a given spring restraint, there is a critical lift velocity beyond which

Left: three diagrams showing how the camshaft profile has evolved; in the early days, it consisted of a circle with a small bump on it; later this bump was widened to keep the valves open as long as was practical; finally ramps were built in to open and close each valve as smoothly as possible, thus imposing minimal strain on the mechanism

the valve will carry on lifting, even though the cam may be dictating a deceleration towards the intended level of maximum lift. This is one way in which valves can be made to clout pistons. The simplest cure is to make the valve lighter, but then you may run into problems of mechanical strength being inadequate. Next best is to fit stronger springs (assuming, to begin with, that the springs are of such number and design as to obviate surge due to their own harmonic sensitivities), but then you increase the loads on the valve seat and throughout the train of components lying between the seat and the camshaft bearings. If this idea does not appeal, then the only solution (short of admitting defeat and running the engine more slowly) is to reprofile the cam so that the valve does not exceed its critical or 'escape' velocity.

Next, we have to consider another factor which can increase the loads on the valve gear. This is the rate of acceleration of the valve (and attendant bits) from its seat. It is obviously desirable that the valve be accelerated as quickly as possible to its limiting velocity: the more urgent its elevation, the more effective is its opening—not only because a sudden opening has a beneficial effect on the generation of pressure and shock waves upon whose exploitation volumentric efficiency so much depends. Nevertheless, there remains the fact that inertia loads on the valve-operating mechanism are another expression of valve acceleration; and clearly there must be mechanical limits to what any particular set of valve gear can stand. Sometimes designers err on the side of caution: in no less celebrated a case than the V16 supercharged BRM, it proved that severe breathing restrictions and consequent failure to realise the anticipated power were due to a pessimistic figure (actually 52,000 ft per sec[2]) adopted for maximum valve acceleration, this limit in turn imposing a deleterious reduction in the valve lift possible.

Limited though they must be, the accelerations to which the valve may be subjected by the cam and paraphernalia lifting it off its seat are considerably more violent than those that can be produced in the opposite direction by any valve springs of tolerable strength.

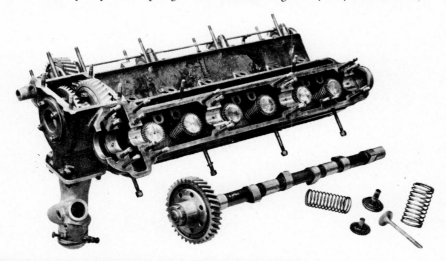

Below: the cylinder head of the Alfa Romeo 6C 1750 Sport, showing the shaft and gear drive to the twin camshafts

Bottom left: the cam block and belt-drive pulley of the Fiat 128

Proportionally longer, then, is the time that must be spent in decelerating the valve; and deceleration, remember, involves not only slowing it down as it comes to the top of its lift but also returning it to its seat. Perhaps it is easier to think of this second or closing phase as positive acceleration downwards, rather than as negative acceleration upwards—if only because we shall then be less confused by the need to abate this acceleration in the final stages of closure, so as to lower the valve as gently as possible onto its seat. If this is not done, then valve and seat will suffer damage, as also will the intervening components of the valve train as the system collapses to produce the clearances normally necessary to allow for differential thermal expansion.

The gradual deceleration is produced by what is commonly called a ramp, a portion of the cam profile that gets gradually nearer to being tangential to the base circle of the cam. It has its counterpart on the opening flank of the cam, which slowly establishes contact with the valve before the full opening acceleration is applied to the system. Without such a ramp, the valve train would have to endure a most almighty and

punishing smack as the essential clearance is taken up —a process bad for ear and engine alike.

These opening and closing ramps are of no little importance to the timing of the valve sequence. The more shallow their gradients, the longer does it take for valve opening to be really effective, and the sooner does the effective closure of the valve occur—in other words, they can shorten the timing, reducing a theoretical duration of opening by as much as 20°. They also make critical the correct adjustment of the tappet clearances: it is not uncommon for an extra 0.01 in of clearance to delay opening and precipitate closure by as much as 20° each, and so reduce total duration of opening from, say, 280° to 240°—a reduction which could be of great relevance to exhaust-system design in a six-cylinder engine.

Already we have said enough to make it clear that the conventional summary of camshaft timing, by reference to the degrees of crankshaft rotation corresponding to the opening and closure of each valve, is inadequate. Taking the DB4 Aston Martin cam as an example, we find that the inlet opens 28° before top dead centre and the exhaust closes 22° after tdc, the exhaust opening 62° before bottom dead centre and the inlet closing 68° after bdc. In the jargon of engineers, this is shorthanded as 28–68–62–22; and you can go further and add up the total duration of opening of each valve, arriving at figures of 276° and 264° for inlet and exhaust valves, respectively. As a first approxi-

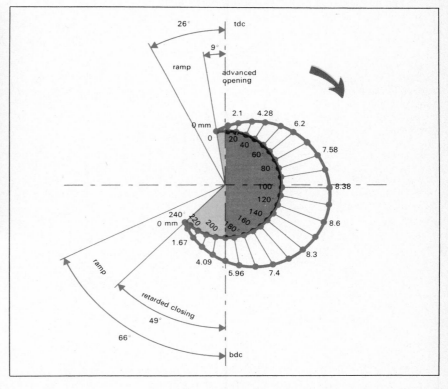

Above: a diagram showing valve lift as a function of crankshaft angle (Abarth Formula Italia); in theory the valve should be open only for 80°, but in practice this has to be enlarged for maximum efficiency

mation, it tells us something, although not much, for we know that, as a general rule, a duration of more than 250° is rather sporting and 300 or more is definitely racy. Likewise, overlap (the interval between inlet opening and exhaust closing) is mild at 30° and very sporting at 80, while 120 puts the engine right into the Formula One class.

Nevertheless, the shorthand 30–70–70–30 business can be very misleading. Properly to see what a cam does, you must look at a graph of lift plotted against crankshaft rotation. From this, you can see and measure the area underneath the curve, the height of

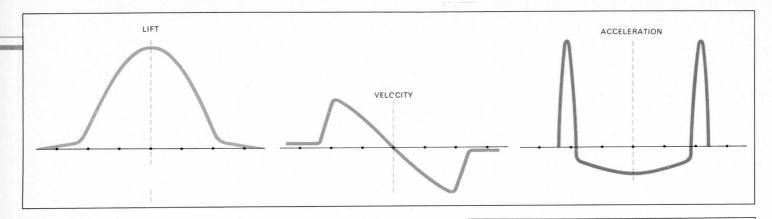

LIFT

VELOCITY

ACCELERATION

Above: graphical representations of the lift, velocity and acceleration of the valve as a function of time; the lift of the valve is dependent not only on cam lift, but on rocker arrangement; the velocity curve should be continuous, because any break indicates that the tappet clearance is too large and is causing knock; it is important that the negative acceleration is not too great, otherwise the valve may cease to follow the profile of the cam

Right: a diagram (top) showing the opening periods of inlet and exhaust valves relative to crankshaft angle; the lower diagrams show how a gauge can be used to check the exact timing of the camshaft by measuring the crankshaft position at which the valves begin to open and reach full closure (in turn measured on a dial gauge)

Bottom right: the 'rubber-band' drive to the primitive camshaft of the 1899 3.5 hp Fiat

which is a measure of the area of valve opening at any chosen instant, and the total area under which is a measure of how much flow can take place during the operation of the cam. By plotting the curves for exhaust and intake cams on the same chart, a clear idea of the value of the overlap can be gathered.

Even these curves can be misleading if they are calculated from the shape of the cam itself. What the valve does, may be, and usually is, rather different from what the cam orders, for the mechanism interposed between these two principal elements is—for all its apparent rigidity—elastic and springy. Rockers flex, pushrods bend, slight compressive tremors occur during heavy accelerations, and the upshot of it all is that at certain points in the cycle the valve may be lagging behind the cam, while at others it may be ahead of it. This has been known for a very long time: the Lorraine Dietrich which did so well at Le Mans in the mid 1920s had very long and very thin pushrods which could be seen flexing, but fortuitously the flexure was such as to improve the valve action at high speeds! Today, it is not unusual for cam profiles to be corrected to take the elasticity of the valve train into account; but the process is fraught with problems, for such corrections cannot be equally effective at all speeds, nor equally effective at all points in the valve train. For instance, if the calculations allow for the flexure of everything, including the rods and rockers, then the tappet itself will be forced to undergo some very rapid and distressing reversals of acceleration, moving the area of accelerated wear and possible damage from the valve to the cam and tappet assembly, where it is usually more difficult to reach and often more expensive to repair.

Now that we know the main problems governing valve motion we can consider how the cam profile is generated so as to produce them. Inaccuracies apart, valve motion is harmonic and may be graphically represented either by a sine wave, in the case of the simplest or harmonic cam (the circular eccentric), or by a combination of parts of different sine waves, as is more common. The main trouble with the simple harmonic cam, whose flanks are compounded from a quartet of circular arcs, is that it makes no provision for the gradual take-up of clearances; although such cams served us well for many years, they are now considered obsolete. The multi-sine-wave cam embodies the necessary opening and closing ramps, and naturally calls for more care in calculation and in manufacture, since there are more curves to be blended into each other. The addition of further corrective curves to deal with discrepancies in valve-train motion complicate the issue still more—although not as much as the seemingly arbitrary decision of certain cam specialists such as Iskenderian to substitute polynomial theorems for the trigonometrical ones from which the harmonic series derive. When this is done, only the prodigious capabilities of the electronic computer make the exercise feasible.   LJKS

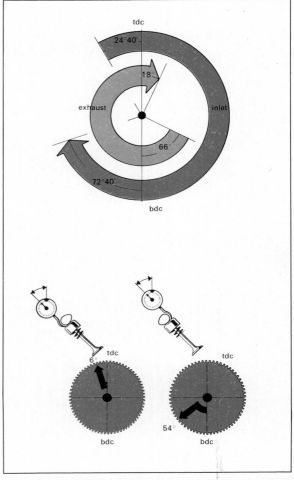

BRITAIN'S ADOPTED COACHBUILDER

Ever since its early history, the Vanden Plas company has been accepted as a manufacturer of luxury and quality products

Above: a superb example of Vanden Plas brougham coachwork, *circa* 1923, complete with carriage lamps and speaking tube. It was fitted to a 6-cylinder Lanchester 21 hp chassis

IT WAS IN 1870 that a blacksmith left his workshop on the industrial north-east side of Brussels to his young nephew Guillame van den Plas; Guillaume decided to specialise, and began making axles for carriages. It was obviously a sensible decision, for soon he had a work-force of nineteen, and in 1884 moved to Antwerp to make complete carriages.

The expansion was speeded up when Guillaume's three sons came into the business, and additional premises were acquired in the 'upper city' of Brussels. Further impetus was added by the advent of the motor car, and in 1903 a new factory was built in Woluwe St Pierre, a suburb to the east of Brussels. As the Belgian motor industry was largely building for export, it was not long before the products of La Carosseri Van den Plas achieved wider acclaim. Their coachwork was often found on German cars, which were imported into England by Captain Theo Masui; a fine landaulette-limousine Van den Plas body on a 20 hp Germain chassis was shown at the 1910 Olympia Show.

Another Belgian marque bodied by Van den Plas was the Métallurgique, and it was on a chassis of that marque that Van den Plas built their 'masterpiece' in convertible coachwork in the spring of 1912. 'The intention of the designers,' commented *Country Life*, 'has been to obtain all the advantages of the full limousine while retaining those of the three-quarter landaulette. At first glance, the car appears to be a limousine, owing to the entire absence of folding stays and to the fact that large lights are fitted to the rear of the doors. When desired, however, the rear part of the body can be folded back, while a section of the roof hinges forward on to the front part between the two doors. Care has been taken to avoid rattling in either the open or closed position. A special feature is the use of frameless glasses for all the windows.'

It was around this time that *The Motor* waxed enthusiastic about a Van den Plas body shown at Olympia: 'There is a red torpedo-shaped tonneau that has speed in its every line, and once seated in it we were loth to get up again, so seductive were the seats . . .' Curiously, Captain Masui was later to lay claim to the invention of the torpedo body, in the light of which the following comment from *Country Life* is perhaps revealing: 'The firm of Theo Masui Limited appear to carry on the ideas initiated by the famous Van den Plas of Brussels, with modifications of their own'. This included, apparently, some of the first all-metal running boards to be used on coachbuilt cars (although they were already a commonplace on the practical, if

Below: in 1925, Vanden Plas were commissioned to produce an open two-door sports body for use on a 3-litre Bentley chassis. This was the completed result

ever humble Model T Ford).

In 1913, according to reports, the Brussels factory, with a workforce of 850, was turning out 750 bodies a year; this, it seems, was insufficient for Captain Masui's requirements for 'genuine' Van den Plas Plas bodies, as in that year he changed the name of his company to Van den Plas (England) Limited, building

Belgian-designed bodies under licence.

When war broke out, the Belgian factory was one of the first to be overrun by the invading Germans. As for the British company, this was taken over by the Aircraft Manufacturing Company of Hendon, and became involved in making aeroplanes.

After the war, the Belgium company began opera-

Right: the interior of the 3-litre Bentley pictured above. The cockpit layout and trim was also the work of Vanden Plas

Opposite page, centre left: a Lanchester Straight 8, with Vanden Plas touring saloon body

Opposite page, centre right: Vanden Plas' Princess 3-litre Mk II luxury saloon of 1962

Opposite page, bottom: the stately 1963 Vanden Plas Princess 4-litre was powered by a 3993 cc engine and weighed 42½ cwt

tions once again, and in the catalogue for the 1920 Brussel's Salon de l'Automobile, it is recorded that the Carrosseri Van den Plas of 30 Rue Saint-Michel, Woluwe, Bruxelles, were exhibiting 'Automobiles', and that H. Van den Plas was a member of the executive committee of the Chambre Syndicale des Constructeurs d'Automobiles & de Cycles de Belgique. Although the Belgium motor industry was not dead, the changed circumstances of the 1920s had diminished its old markets, and henceforth the focus of attention would be on its moribund English subsidiary, which had busied itself building bodies for the Leyland Eight before AMC's failure.

The Aircraft Manufacturing Company had gone into liquidation as a result of the fall in demand for aircraft after the Armistice; one of the company's managers, Edwin Fox, believed in the potential of a revived British Van den Plas coachbuilding company, and made an offer of £30,000 (most of which would have been borrowed capital) to the company's receivers. The bid was unsuccessful, but there can have been no other offers for AMC, as some considerable time later Edwin Fox acquired the name, goodwill and work in hand for £6000, raised by himself and his two brothers.

Vanden Plas (England) 1923, Limited, needed a new factory, and in 1923 acquired Kingsbury Works. The Hyde, Hendon, London NW9, which had been standing empty for some time after the liquidator's stocks of Kingsbury Junior light cars had been cleared following the failure of the Kingsbury Engineering Company in 1921. Prior to the building of Kingsbury

building bodies for luxury American chassis. At the 1930 Olympia Show, the company's British agents, Lendrum & Hartman, exhibited an enclosed drive limousine-landaulette de luxe on a sixteen-cylinder Cadillac chassis ('a very roomy and comfortable carriage for any purpose') and a seven-seater limousine on an eight-cylinder Buick chassis.

Below: delightful use of colour emphasised the harmonious lines of this 1938/9 Alvis 4.3-litre tourer with coachwork by Vanden Plas. The car topped 100 mph

cars and motor cycles, the factory had been operated by the brothers Ernest and Harold Barningham as a manufactory of aircraft parts.

The Kingsbury Works, on the edge of Kingsbury aerodrome, was built in the grounds of Kingsbury House, an early Victorian mansion, all of which were purchased by Edwin Fox as Vanden Plas prospered and grew. The company first exhibited at Olympia in 1924, when they showed a seven-seater limousine on a long-chassis Renault 45 and a 3-litre Bentley saloon. The Renault, upholstered in calfskin and with external trim in sham cane, was over seventeen feet long; the Bentley, which had four-door coachwork had all the bright work silver-plated. A third Vanden Plas body, a sporting open tourer painted ivory white with dark blue wings and chassis was shown on the stand of Bentley Motors Limited; Vanden Plas leased part of the Kingsbury Estate to Bentley, and their coachwork became associated with this marque. Almost a quarter of all Cricklewood Bentleys, including all five Le Mans winners, were bodied by Vanden Plas. Special coachwork was also fitted to other quality chassis such as Delage, Talbot, Daimler and Lanchester.

Surprisingly, the Belgian Van den Plas Company was still operating in 1930, although by that time it was

Right: the Vanden Plas 1500 Automatic of 1974 was a luxury version of British Leyland's Austin Allegro model. It had a number of refinements not available on standard Allegros, such as leather seats and a walnut dashboard

Below: a favourite with wealthy customers wanting luxury and elegance was the Daimler Limousine of the mid-1970s. It was powered by the six-cylinder Jaguar 4.2-litre XK-series motor and its coachwork was the product of Vanden Plas

At this period, the English company was concentrating on Weymann-type bodies, but by 1931 it seemed that they had reverted to traditional methods of construction. At that year's Olympia Show, they exhibited a Talbot 90, a 13 hp Invicta Tourer and a 3-litre Lagonda Coupé. Vanden Plas coachwork was used on the three Talbots which won a Coupe des Alpes in the 1932 International Alpine Trial; as a consequence, a special series of Coupe des Alpes replica bodies was built on Talbot chassis. The 1932 Olympia Show also saw the beginning of an association with Alvis, for which company Vanden Plas manufactured special sporting bodies throughout the 1930s. It was perhaps not coincidental that Edwin Fox's son Roland, who had studied motor-body engineering at the London Polytechnic before moving to Geneva as a draughtsman with Carrosserie Gangloff, spent most of the 1930s as body engineer with Alvis before becoming Works Director of Vanden Plas in 1939.

During the war years, Vanden Plas was once again involved in aircraft work, particularly in the construction of the all-wood De Havilland Mosquito. The company had to tool up for large-scale war-time production, and it was felt that this experience should not be wasted when peace came. Edwin and Roland Fox heard that the Austin Motor Company was looking for a manufacturer for a coachbuilt saloon body for its new 4-litre chassis. They began discussions which resulted in Vanden Plas becoming a subsidiary of Austin in June 1946.

A prototype body was designed, built, accepted without alteration and ready for its public début at the Geneva Motor Show in March 1947. Known as the Austin A135 Princess, the model was updated regularly and supplemented from 1952 by a long-wheelbase limousine version.

Edwin Fox died in 1954 and his son became Managing Director. Four years later, Vanden Plas became a marque in its own right, the name being used

Below: the 1975 Daimler 4.2-litre Landaulette with coachwork by Vanden Plas. Examples were ordered by a number of governments for use by leading statesmen and dignitaries

not only for the big saloons and limousines but also for luxury versions of the Austin A99/A110 series and the 1100, these models being superseded by the 4-litre Rolls-Royce engined R and 1300 respectively.

In 1974, the Princess name was dropped from Vanden Plas nomenclature with the announcement of the Vanden Plas 1500, a luxury version of the Austin Allegro. At the same time, Roland Fox retired (although continuing to act in an advisory capacity for the company) and was succeeded by W. H. Peel, who had been with Vanden Plas since 1946.

However, the Vanden Plas name was still associated with luxury limousines, their 1975 offering in this field being a special super-luxury version of the Daimler XJ Double-six and the Limousine. The landaulette version of the Daimler Limousine could cost up to £15,000, and the complex linkage of the folding roof could involve some 300 hours of building and adjustment by craftsmen.

The standards followed in the new car stem from the sense of continuity apparent in all Vanden Plas products since the firm's foundation.   PD

Below: the 1973 Vanden Plas 1300; this was a luxury version of the Austin/Morris 1300 model range

YWL 669L

THE AMERICAN MARATHON

The Vanderbilt Cup realised the dreams of a rich man, dedicated enough to make them come true

'AS FOOLISH AS A BULLFIGHT; as vulgar as reddening the sands in a gladiatorial contest; as revolting as bartering Christ's garments for a few pieces of silver!' fulminated the Reverend Newell Dwight Hills on learning that young William Kissem Vanderbilt was sponsoring a motor race on the hitherto peaceful rural roads of Long Island, New York State, in 1904.

Not that Willie gave a damn for the Reverend Hills's opinion, for he was both wealthy enough and enthusiastic enough to disregard such facile criticism. Great-grandson of the founder of the Vanderbilt dynasty, William Kissem had been a keen supporter of motoring as early as 1895, when he was an eighteen-year-old Harvard student, and had given 3000 francs to the prize fund for the Paris–Bordeaux race. He began to participate in automobile sport around 1900, and by 1902 had acquired a Mercédès on which he became the first man officially to travel faster than 60 mph, on the Achères Road near Paris. He then acquired an 80 hp Mors with which he competed in the Paris–Vienna and Circuit des Ardennes in 1902 and in the Paris–Madrid in 1903.

The year 1904 saw the acquisition of a 90 hp Mercédès with a speed potential in excess of 100 mph —indeed, Vanderbilt claimed to have achieved this speed before Rigolly's Gobron-Brillié became the first officially timed car to break the 100 mph barrier—and

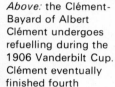

Above: the Clément-Bayard of Albert Clément undergoes refuelling during the 1906 Vanderbilt Cup. Clément eventually finished fourth

Left: Harding's Hayes cornering at speed during the 1906 Vanderbilt Cup. Victory in this event went to Wagner's 100 hp, 12.7-litre Darracq at a speed of 61.4 mph

the donation of a 31-inch Tiffany loving cup to the American Automobile Club, to be competed for by teams of the top international marques and drivers. There was more than a hint of the Gordon Bennett about the regulations for the Vanderbilt Cup Race—hardly surprising, as James Gordon Bennett was a close friend of Willie K.

Held on Saturday 8 October 1904, over a triangular course about thirty miles long, and based on public turnpike roads, the first Vanderbilt Cup race attracted an entry of eighteen—six French, five American, five German and two Italian. While the rules of the race specified that all parts of the competing cars had to be made in their country of origin, there was no stipulation that drivers had to be of the same nationality as their cars. So George Heath, an American resident in Paris, drove one of the French Panhards, and three of the five Mercédès competing were driven by Americans.

Local opposition to the race remained fierce until it was tempered by the realisation that the wealthy spectators who flocked to the event were willing to pay up to $25 for a good parking place near the circuit—and as an estimated 50,000 spectators turned up to watch the race, the locals quickly learned to temper their hostile feelings with cupidity.

First away in the race was Al Campbell, driving a 60 hp Mercédès, followed at two-minute intervals by the rest of the entry. The course, which mostly covered dirt roads treated with oil to lay the dust, was intersected by six level crossings, and proved a real car-breaker. Wilhelm Werner, driving Clarence Gray Dinsmore's 12-litre 90 hp Mercédès, damaged his brakes pulling up for a crossing, while Hawley's Mercédès 60 smashed its front springs taking a crossing too fast. Both Fiats fell out within a lap with transmission failure, while Frank Croker (son of the notorious Boss Croker who ran the Tammany Hall political racket in New York State) had drilled so much metal out of his 75 hp Simplex to lighten it, that the car gently began to fold in the middle as it pounded over the course. It was still running when the race ended, but its gearbox was trailing in the road!

Considering the total lack of crowd discipline—there were only 100 policemen to control the thirty-mile course—and the reported predilection of spectators for dropping broken glass and tintacks into the road, it is surprising that only one fatality occurred. George Arents Jr, whose wild driving had given the lie to his avowed statement that he knew the course so well that he had no need to practice, lost a front tyre from his 60 hp Mercédès on the second lap. The bare rim jammed in a tramline, flipping the car over on to its back and killing the mechanic, Mensel.

The battle for first place was closely fought between Heath's Panhard and Albert Clément's Clément-Bayard for most of the ten-lap race; Heath took the lead on the penultimate lap and finished well ahead of the young Clément. Once these two cars had crossed the finishing line, the spectators lost interest, and wandered on to the track, and the race had to be stopped. Lying third and fourth on elapsed time were the two smallest cars in the race, Herb Lytle's 24 hp Pope-Toledo and Charles Schmidt's 30 hp Packard, *Grey Wolf*. Heath's average for the race had been 52.2 mph, and he had covered the distance in five hours 26 minutes 45 seconds.

The crowd problem was even worse the following year, when the course was altered to run north, not south, of the Jericho Turnpike, thus eliminating the speed controls through populated areas that had slowed the 1904 event.

So many American entries were received that it was decided to hold Eliminating Trials to choose the home team. The trials were duly won by Dingley's Pope-Toledo, Nutt's Haynes, Robert's Thomas, Jardine's Royal and Tracy's Locomobile; but two day's later the decision was overturned, and the Royal, the Haynes and the Thomas were ousted by the Cup Race Commission, who thought that Lytle's Pope-Toledo, a 60 hp front-wheel-drive Christie and a 40 hp White Steamer would make a more spectacular showing in the race proper.

And so in one instance it proved. Vincenzo Lancia was firmly in the lead in the eighth lap when he pulled away from his pits just in front of the Christie, which was snaking down the road at top speed; the American car hit the rear wheels of Lancia's Fiat and crashed into a field, killing the mechanic. The crowd's adulation for Lancia turned to hostility, and the damage to his car cost him the race, which went to Héméry's 80 hp Darracq, followed by Heath's Panhard and Tracy's Locomobile. Lancia finished fourth and, once again, the crowd, which was four or five-times greater than it had been the previous year, caused the race to be halted by swarming on to the track.

The 1906 Vanderbilt was run over virtually the same course as the previous year's race, although in contrast, the Eliminating Trials were fairly organised, the only substitution being that of Lawwell's 110 hp air-cooled Frayer-Miller for Lytle's 120 hp Pope-Toledo, disqualified because it had had to be tow-started. So, the American line-up was: Lawwell, Tracy (Locomobile), Le Blon (Thomas), Harding (Haynes) and Christie (Christie). Against them were lined up Heath (Panhard), Clément (Clément), Duray (De Diétrich), Wagner (Darracq) and Shepard (Hotchkiss) representing France, Jenatzy and Luttgen on Mercédès for Germany, and Lancia, Nazzaro and Weilschott on FIATs and Cagno and Fabry on Italas for Italy. Wagner's 100 hp, 12.7-litre Darracq led all the way but, once again, it was the crowd which dominated the race, blocking the road on the dangerous corners, and only parting like the waters of the Red Sea as a car approached. Miraculously, only one spectator was killed, when Shepard (who was Willie K's cousin) smashed into a crowd estimated at 20,000 which was blocking the notorious Krug's Corner.

In those circumstances, Wagner's winning speed of 61.4 mph is all the more remarkable; second and third were Lancia and Duray, who had fought neck-and-neck through the race, followed by Clément, Jenatzy and Nazzaro. And then, yet again, the crowd ended it by pushing on to the track.

This was the last of the true open-road Vanderbilts; there was no race in 1907, and in 1908 the partly completed Long Island Motor Parkway, a privately constructed toll road, which was to permit Vanderbilt and his rich friends to commute into New York without fear of being prosecuted for speeding, was used as the basis for the Cup course, with steeply banked corners, there were wire fences to keep the spectators at bay. However, they came armed with wire-cutters, and things were as bad as ever. Hoses had to be used to clear the crowd from the pits before the race could start.

Hot favourite was George Robertson, driving a two-year-old Locomobile 90, with which Tracy had contested the 1906 Vanderbilt, while other leading contenders were Lytle (Isotta-Fraschini), Strang (Renault) and Chevrolet (Matheson). Willie Haupt's Chadwick was in with a chance, too, and led the mid-section of the race before being eliminated by ignition troubles.

Top: George Heath, an American who lived in Paris, corners his French Panhard during the 1906 Vanderbilt Cup at Long Island. Two years earlier, in 1904, Heath drove his Panhard to victory in the Vanderbilt Cup series

Above: George Robertson poses at the wheel of his Locomobile prior to the start of the 1908 Vanderbilt Cup event. Robertson went on to win the race, thus becoming the first American driver in an American car ever to win an International motor sporting event

It was Robertson who won, though, coming in two minutes ahead of Lytle to record the first all-American victory in an international motor race. It is recorded that, during the race, Robertson, unable to pass a slower car whose mechanic was not looking to the rear, told his mechanic to hurl a hammer at the offender to make him move over!

After the first two cars had crossed the line, the crowd, true to form, flooded on to the track and caused the race to be halted.

The 1909 and 1910 Vanderbilts were held on the same course, but as they were restricted to stock cars, they were less interesting; both were won by the same car/driver combination, Harry Grant in an Alco, a French Berliet built under licence.

In 1911, the Vanderbilt was exiled to Savannah to escape the suicidal spectators of Long Island, and won by Ralph Mulford (Lozier); in 1912, the race found a home in Milwaukee, where Ralph dePalma won in a Mercédès. Nobody wanted the Vanderbilt in 1913, but in 1914 the race was held on the Santa Monica Circuit near Los Angeles, and again won by de Palma and his veteran Mercédès. Dario Resta and his Peugeot carried off the 1915 and 1916 Vanderbilts, which took place at San Francisco and Santa Monica. After that, Willie K. took back his trophy and retired it, as he felt that the old spirit of the race had gone.

However, when, in the mid 1930s an artificial road-racing circuit, the Roosevelt Raceway, was opened in New York State, another Vanderbilt, George this time, offered a cup for international competition. It was won in 1936 by Nuvolari and in 1937 by Rosemeyer.

A third Vanderbilt Cup made its appearance in 1960 when Willie K's nephew, Cornelius, gave a cup for the revival of road-racing at the Roosevelt Raceway, which had become a horse-trotting track. The race was a fiasco, however, and from 1961 the Vanderbilt Cup was loaned to the Bridgehampton Road Race Circuit for presentation to the winner of the first sports-car race of the season. DBW

THE END OF AN ERA

The Vanwalls were the last front-engined cars to win the Manufacturer's Championship

FEW CARS HAVE PLAYED so significant a part in the history of motor racing as the Vanwall, which marked the end of a long beginning to the Grand Prix aspirations of British motor-racing enthusiasts, and the beginning of the end of the classical era in the sport. It was the first British car ever to effectively challenge the best of continental opposition in Grand Prix racing, the first British car to win the Manufacturers' World Championship, and the first on which Colin Chapman was to try his skills in the Formula One circus before entering the arena with a car bearing his own Lotus imprint. Its mechanical inspirations came from many sources, including BRM, Norton, Rolls-Royce and numerous specialists, brought in one at a time until finally everything was more or less right; but it was the persistence and zeal of its sponsor Mr G. A. Vandervell that brought the whole project to fruition in the course of six years.

Vandervell ran a firm making bearings. After acquiring the idea of thin-walled plain bearings from the Napier aero-engine factory across the road from his own premises at Acton, Vandervell developed the idea to make his company rich and, as we shall see, indispensable. He was also a director of the Norton motor-cycle company, and in the early days of the BRM project he was active in lending his aid. He did not long maintain his connection with BRM, for he was unable to work happily with their organisation; but while there, he arranged for them to investigate the possibilities of a water-cooled version of the Norton racing motor-cycle engine as a feasibility study of potential future value, should circumstances change to make the supercharged V16 BRM no longer useful in racing. The single-cylinder experimental engine that resulted, although structurally different from the Norton cylinder head and ports, and the valve mechanism was identical. The engine could sustain 4 bhp more than the Norton air-cooled original could give in shorts bursts—so when, in 1952, Vandervell set about the construction of his own racing car in a spate of sporting enthusiasm and patriotic fervour, this experimental 'wet Norton' constituted the basic module around which its engine could be designed.

What Vandervell had in mind was clearly an engine that was a multiple of Manx Nortons unified by a common crankcase, and to do the necessary engineering of the materials by which the Norton holes might be defined, he engaged the gifted Polish engineer Leo Kusmicki, who came from Norton and subsequently joined Rootes where he remains, at the time of writing, in the service of Chrysler. Kusmicki kept the four cylinders independent in construction, but surrounded them by a common water jacket, and surmounted them by a single common cylinder-head casting incorporating valve gear that was an exact copy of the Norton original, which meant that the upper extremities of the valve stems were open to the gaze of the curious because exposed hairpin valve springs bore

Right: bird's-eye view of the 1957 18 Vanwall Grand Prix car, probably the last truly successful front-engined Formula One machine ever built; it was powered by a 2.5-litre, four-cylinder motor and was also the first British car effectively to challenge the best of the great Continental teams such as Ferrari and Maserati

upon them, with cylindrical tappets set in cam boxes mounted above them in a clerestory construction that allowed the cooling air to enter in generous measures, and the lubricating oil to depart, likewise. The induction system naturally incorporated four Amal motorcycle racing carburettors, and so Vandervell had, for the top half of his Formula Two engine, a four-cylinder two-litre multi-Norton; but what was he going to do for a bottom half? The high internal stresses consequent upon the use of only four rather long-stroke cylinders appeared to be within the capacity of the crankcase of the smallest of the Rolls-Royce 'B' series of engines which had been developed with an eye to military contracts. Severing the crankcase from its superstructure, and casting it in aluminium-alloy rather than iron, produced a structure sufficiently robust for the purpose, and little modification of the Rolls-Royce crankshaft would be necessary. Thus, the Vanwall engine could be built up from components whose reliability and performance potential were already known.

Even less originality was shown in the matter of chassis design which was frankly copied from the current Ferrari; but this was not the only feature to hamper its progress. By the time the car was a runner, the Formula Two for which it was intended had lapsed, and the new 1954 Formula One, admitting engines of $2\frac{1}{2}$ litres capacity, made the Vanwall subject to an unnecessarily self-imposed handicap. Increasing its capacity by 10 per cent did nothing to make the 1954 season a successful one, the car suffering from numerous troubles with the cooling system, with the front suspension and with the fuel system, although its disc brakes—a Vanwall-made version of a Goodyear design—were satisfactory from the very beginning and were to remain so throughout the car's career.

The first big change was made for the 1955 season with the substitution of fuel injection for carburation, the Amal carburettor bodies remaining to serve merely as throttling devices. Vandervell wanted Bosch injection, but Bosch had of course supplied similar systems for the Mercedes-Benz Grand Prix car that was almost undisputed master of the circuits at that time, and were naturally reluctant to play fast and loose with the mighty Daimler-Benz Company. The latter on the other hand was soon embarrassed by a telephone call from Mr Vandervell making it clear that if he could not have Bosch injection, they could not have any of his bearings; and thus the problem was resolved. It was not the first time, incidentally, that Daimler-Benz had been stymied by the business tactics of Britain's motor industry: when they sought disc brakes from Dunlop some years earlier, their custom had been refused because they would have been competing with Jaguar, whose sports-racing cars scored some notable victories with their aid.

In fact, Bosch had awful trouble with the Vanwall engine: unlike the smooth-running straight-eight Mercedes-Benz, the Vanwall was as rough as any other big in-line four, and the vibration wrought havoc with the high-pressure fuel lines, as well as being responsible for many infuriating derangements of the throttle linkages, these faults being responsible for many retirements in racing. Even when the car was running well it was at a disadvantage because its capacity was 12 per cent less than that of its rivals, so for 1956 it was increased to a full $2\frac{1}{2}$ litres, with other necessary modifications to the engine being perforce accepted, such as the change in the included angle of the valves from the Norton's 77° to a more modest 60°. More importantly, the rest of the car underwent a complete metamorphosis. Chapman was called in as a consultant

to design an entirely new chassis, and evolved a space frame typical of what was then his current work, a confection of small-diameter tubes triangulated so that all loads were distributed either in tension or compression through the frame members, the elimination of bending stresses allowing lighter tubing to be employed. He also reduced the unsprung mass of the De Dion rear axle, and provided for precise control of its movement and location of the rear roll centre by using a Watt linkage to supply lateral constraint. The four-speed gearbox was modified as far as it could be, an extra bottom gear allowing effective starting-line sprints without depriving the car of the high gear ratios needed on the faster circuits, and Porsche synchromesh made the driver's task easier in engaging the top four ratios. Adding an anti-roll torsion bar to the front suspension, Chapman pronounced the work complete, but the car's only notable success during the season was in winning a Formula One race (not of Grand Prix status) at Silverstone against sparse opposition that included two Ferrari-Lancia V8 cars. Later and more significant races showed that the handling was still imperfect, so for 1957 Chapman completely revised the rear suspension, adopting all the established means of inducing understeer, including a steeply inclined roll axis and the provision of 3 degrees of negative camber for the rear wheels on their De Dion axle beam. Despite all this, the handling qualities of the Vanwall remained somewhat imperfect, especially at the Nürburgring, where its suspension travel ($2\frac{1}{2}$ inches at the front, 2 inches at the rear) was somewhat inadequate. Nevertheless, in 1957 the Vanwall proved itself one of the fastest, and in the right circumstances the very fastest, of Grand Prix cars. Much of this tremendous performance was due to the entirely new bodywork that had been created during the preceding season by Frank Costin, the de Havilland aerodynamicist working on Chapman's Lotus cars.

The Vanwall presented Costin with apparently insuperable problems. The frontal area of the car was substantial, its height bordering on the ridiculous. The driver's seat could not be brought closer than thirteen inches to the ground, for it was above the gearbox; the transmission line could not be lowered without wasting some of the engine's prized 290 bhp; and with everything taken into account, the top of the driver's helmet was about fifty inches above ground level. In any case, the engine was not only tall, but was also set well forward in the chassis, forcing the bonnet line to be very high, and so the driver had to sit even

Above: Tony Vandervell's financial fortune was due to the success gained by his company's thin-walled bearings; in an attempt to promote these bearings, Vandervell purchased a racing single-seater Ferrari and christened it the 'Thin-wall Special'. Driven by such competitors as Reg Parnell, the car provided much publicity for Vandervell's company

higher if he were to see over it. Costin knew that a square foot of frontal area was worth yards of streamlining, but he could see here a case for concentrating on good penetration and air flow. The result was a remarkably broad and bulbous shape which was nevertheless beautifully curvilinear and smooth, drag being minimised in every possible way, and everything possible being enclosed. The only excrescences were the four wheels and the top of the driver's head. The barter of frontal area for improved air flow proved to be justified: the Vanwall was much faster in a straight line than any of its rivals.

To be fair, its engine gave rather more power than theirs. The difference was not more than 10 bhp in the case of the Ferrari-Lancia, and this discrepancy could not possibly account for the absurd difference in the car's maximum speeds. Thus, in 1957 the Vanwall became really and truly competitive, starting by leading the Syracuse GP and establishing a new lap record, then putting in the fastest practice lap at Monaco and leading the race until its brakes failed. By the time of the French GP, the metal fuel pipes for the high-pressure injection system were replaced by flexible tubing built to aircraft standards by the Palmer company, and combined with a new throttle linkage to eliminate most of the old troubles. The linkage did in fact turn traitor on Brooks in the Italian GP of 1957, a meeting at which three of the four cars on the front line were Vanwalls, while the fourth was there not because it was a Maserati but because it was driven by Fangio. The Vanwall driven by Moss kept going when that of Brooks faltered, having so much time in hand by the 77th lap that he could afford to make a precautionary pit stop for rear wheels and oil, and still win by 41 seconds. The year ended with Moss second in the World Championship to Fangio, having become the first Englishman ever to win the British GP in a British car.

It was the last year in which anything other than petrol could be used for fuelling a Grand Prix machine. The compulsory use of petrol in 1958 was particularly hard on Vanwall, whose need of alcohol as an internal engine coolant was no more urgent than its need of it as a mitigator of the imperfections of contemporary fuel injection apparatus. Frenzied work on mixture control eventually resulted in the 1958 engine recovering some of its reliability, despite a 200°C increase in exhaust-valve temperature, but the engineers had to reconcile themselves to a loss of power. Whereas in 1957 the alcoholic engine developed 290 bhp at 7500 rpm, in 1958 the petrol-burner ran up to the same

speed (not unaturally, since it was mechanical stresses that imposed the limit) but generated only 262 bhp.

While many others were in like predicament, Ferrari had a new engine designed from the outset for petrol, so the 1958 Ferrari Dino 246 had a good 280 bhp. Moreover, it was lighter, and more compact than the Vanwall, and if not in fact as fast, it was more reliable in its engine, enabling Hawthorn to become World Champion driver in 1958, although by only one point ahead of Moss in the Vanwall. Still, it was no longer necessary to look to driver championships for a clue to the potentiality of their cars, for in 1958 a manufacturers' championship was instigated, and the Vanwall emerged clear victor with the maximum possible number of points scored (48), whereas Ferrari could muster but 40. If the Ferrari was a new car, the Vanwall was a changed one, not only in the motor system but also in its handling. The rear wheels were deprived of their negative camber, the front anti-roll bar was reduced in thickness, and stiffer wheels of convuluted disc pattern were used either at the rear or at all four hubs, in which latter case the original deliberate understeer was even more reduced. Far more important than any of these alterations was the change in tyres, for 1958 saw the departure from racing of Pirelli (whose racing tyres had previously been the best) and the introduction of a new nylon-cord Dunlop R5—as significant an improvement over the established rayon carcass as that had been over the earlier cotton type.

For all these reasons, the 1958 Vanwall, although 10 per cent less powerful than the 1957 one, was often faster. Some of the improvement could be attributed to better handling, some of it to improvement in the tyres, and the rest to intensive work done on the fuel-injection system in the process of converting to petrol, for the engine was now receiving a more accurately metered dosage than previously, and the old flat spots in its power curve had been eliminated. The high racing ratios in the gearbox (1, 1.12, 1.4 and 1.96:1) made it unnecessary for the driver to let the engine rpm drop below 6700 in top, 5900 in fourth, or 5400 in third gear, while observing the mandatory 7500 maximum; but at a circuit such as the Nürburgring, where the engine speed could easily be allowed to drop to the 5000 mark where the worst of the flat spots was in 1957, the revised Vanwall was much more drivable, which may explain why Moss was able to reduce his best 1957 lap by no less than 6 per cent in the succeeding year.

It is interesting to speculate on how the Vanwall would have faired in 1959, with due improvements and amendments such as might have been carried out during the winter, in competition with the new style of cars which set at nought the accepted tenets of high polar moment of inertia in front-engined understeering cars, and confirmed the superiority of a new breed of rear-engined racers. Unfortunately, the severe illness of Mr Vandervell made it necessary for the activities of the Vanwall racing team to be suspended and, although an unwieldy rear-engined device made its appearance in the hands of Surtees on one or two occasions later, no serious work was done. The Vanwall was not the last front-engined Grand Prix car, for Aston Martin and BRM continued the line in 1959, and Ferrari persevered with this layout until 1961, in company with the ingenious but unsuccessful Scarab from America. Nevertheless, the Vanwall was the last front-engined Grand Prix car to be an unquestionable success, and earned a secure place in history as the culmination of 52 years of the classical tradition in Grand Prix racing. LJKS

Below: Stirling Moss in action in the 1958 Grand Prix Vanwall; although Moss lost the World Drivers' Championship to Mike Hawthorn by a single point, the Vanwall team captured the prestigious Manufacturer's Championship

In Nuvolaris shadow

DOUR, UNSMILING AND WORLDLY, Achille Varzi was one of the greatest drivers of his day, but fate had singled him out to play a kind of *Fidus Achates* to Tazio Nuvolari, and so it was inevitable that he should be overshadowed by the extrovert personality of his contemporary.

Born in 1904, the son of a comfortably off textile manufacturer in Galliate, near Milan, Varzi first came to public notice as a motor cyclist (as indeed was his brother Angelo), riding Sunbeam and Garelli machines. Varzi's cold, calculating, precise style contrasted vividly with the ebullience of Nuvolari, and both were given top billing during 1924, although, oddly enough, they rarely appeared together.

In 1924, Varzi was the first Italian to enter for the Isle of Man TT, riding a Dot-Bradshaw, and was well up with the leaders when he was forced to run off the road to avoid a rider who had fallen off ahead of him. For this 'brave and sporting action' he was awarded the Nisbet Trophy.

In 1927, Nuvolari and Varzi entered into partnership to form a racing stable of Type 35 Bugattis, which made its début at the 1928 Tripoli Grand Prix. Varzi took Guido Bignami as mechanic, an association which was to last

throughout Varzi's racing career (Bignami subsequently became Fangio's mechanic). Varzi took the lead at an early stage, but Nuvolari fought back, and eventually Varzi was slowed by ignition trouble, and finished third. After only a few races, Varzi felt that his style was being cramped by Nuvolari, so he took advantage of the family finances to buy himself a P2 Alfa Romeo, and set up on his own late in 1928. In the Italian GP, marred by Materassi's tragic crash, Varzi came second, ahead of his erstwhile partner, and during 1929 won so many victories that Nuvolari was stung into buying a P2 so that he could compete on the same terms. In the Coppa Montenero at Leghorn, Varzi finished no less than two minutes ahead of Nuvolari, who was driving encased in plaster as the result of a crash in the Coppa del Mare motor-cycle race that occurred only a week earlier.

The 1930 Mille Miglia saw Varzi, driving an Alfa 1750 sports car, outsmarted by Nuvolari's driving tactics, to be beaten by a matter of seconds; but he took his revenge in the Targa Florio. By now, Varzi had become a member of the Alfa works team, and had sold his P2 racer

Varzi winning the 1934 Targa in his Alfa 2900B

Varzi helps to refuel his car at Modena in 1934

to the company; but he drove this racing car in the Targa (which was really a sports-car event) and won at record speed.

Nuvolari joined Alfa Romeo in 1930 and, predictably, Varzi left, to join the rising star of Maserati, winning the Coppa Acerbo on his first time out with his new car. He was also victorious in the Spanish and Italian Grands Prix, as well as coming third in an Alfa 1750 in the Ulster TT. These achievements earned him the title of Champion of Italy for the season.

For 1931, there was yet another change of mount, this time to a 2.3-litre Bugatti Type 51, with which he won at Tunis, Alessandria and the French GP; 1932 was not such a good season, with only one victory, at Tunis, combined with retirement in the Mille Miglia and in the Monaco Grand Prix.

Varzi was back on form in 1933, with the 4.9-litre Bugatti Type 54, and the Monaco Grand Prix saw a most exciting duel between the Bugatti and Nuvolari's Scuderia Ferrari Alfa, with the two men fighting for supremacy for 99 out of the hundred laps. On the final circuit, Varzi jabbed the gear lever into third, and held it

there, gunning his engine at well over the safety limit to take the lead. Nuvolari responded with similar tactics, but his engine burst into flames and he had to abandon it fifty yards from the finishing line. The Tripoli GP was another close-fought battle between the two rivals, again ending in a win for Varzi; but the event was not as competitive as it might have been, for several of the other drivers had agreed to hold back and give Varzi a clear run through the field in exchange for a percentage of the prize money from the winning lottery ticket.

It was back to Alfa for 1934, and in a Scuderia Ferrari car, Varzi won the Mille Miglia, having wisely equipped his machine with wet-weather tyres to compensate for the appalling conditions. With a 2.9-litre Alfa racer, Varzi took nine firsts and several other good places during the season, although at Modena, on the Ferrari team's home ground, Nuvolari's Maserati overtook Varzi with sufficient ease for the *Flying Mantuan* to cock a snook at his rival as he passed.

Nuvolari rejoined the Scuderia Ferrari in 1935, but Varzi moved on, to drive one of the new and treacherous rear-engined Auto-Unions. He won his first race with this model, the Tunis

GP in May, but the cars seemed dogged by minor development troubles during the rest of the season.

In 1936, Varzi took second place in the Monaco GP, despite torrential rain, then won at Tripoli with a record lap of nearly 142 mph. The following week, though, at Tunis, Varzi had his first-ever racing crash. There were no more outright victories that season; however, there was a third in the Hungarian GP at Budapest and a narrow defeat by Nuvolari in the Italian GP in Monza Park, in which Varzi had entered his Auto-Union as a privateer.

Indeed, it seemed as though Varzi's career had passed its peak: he was out of racing for much of 1937 (it was rumoured there was a woman in the case), although he won the San Remo Voiturette GP in a Maserati 6CM. His health was said to be bad, there was talk of drug addiction, and Varzi did not make a comeback to his old form until 1946, with an Alfa Romeo 158. But, after two successful seasons, Varzi skidded on a rain-soaked track while practicing for the Swiss GP on the Bremgarten circuit, and was killed instantly.   DBW

ONE OF BRITAIN'S 'BIG FOUR'

Vauxhall are General Motors' division in Great Britain and of the quartet that also includes Chrysler, British Leyland and Ford

FULK LE BRÉANT was a loyal and true subject of King John, and loyalty and truth could find pretty direct rewards in those days. The grateful monarch gave Fulk the manor of Luton for his soldiering services, plus an heiress to be his bride. The lady, Margaret de Redvers, brought with her a house at Lambeth, which in those days was well up-river of London.

When not hawking and hunting through the deer forests around Luton, Fulk resided at his new property at Lambeth. The house became known locally as Fulk's Hall . . . and it was to this spot, long after Fulk (who was exiled to France in 1216 and died a poor man) and his London 'pad' had passed into history and the name had been re-shaped by centuries of local usage first into Fawke's Hall and then into Vauxhall, that a Scottish engineer called Alexander Wilson came to found an ironworks in 1857.

Wilson's Vauxhall Ironworks specialised in steam engines for river craft, and many a Thames tug and paddle steamer toward the end of the nineteenth century was Vauxhall Ironworks powered. But by the last decade of the century, Wilson was in financial difficulties, and the receivers decided to gamble by getting in on the ground floor of the horseless-carriage business that was clearly developing as the thing of the future.

The firm had already been experimenting with petrol engines for river launches, so was not going into the business entirely 'cold'. Accordingly, the first Vauxhall Ironworks car of 1903 was fairly well conceived: a 5 hp horizontal single-cylinder tiller-steered chain-driven runabout rather in the American style. Its price was £130, fuel consumption was around 40 mpg, and 43 examples were built. At the time of writing, two exist, one of them in the London Science Museum.

The following year this model was modified with tiller steering giving way to a steering wheel—76 were sold—and in 1905 two new models were introduced, one with three cylinders, of 1.8 litres producing 7/9 hp, and the other a four-cylinder 2.4-litre car giving 18 hp. These engines had mechanically operated inlet valves, and boasted a reverse gear. Their bonnets were characterised by fluting around the top edges.

During 1905, the Vauxhall Ironworks made a big move, forsaking the little factory in Vauxhall Walk and moving to the small Midlands town of Luton—Fulk's old country seat. Nothing in the documentation of the day exists to suggest that this was anything other than a coincidence. At any rate, the Mediaeval warrior's heraldic emblem was raised at Luton after an absence of seven centuries, for Alexander Wilson had chosen for his Vauxhall Ironworks trademark Fulk's griffin, half eagle, half lion.

Right: the second Vauxhall produced was this 6 hp single-cylinder of 1904; the car, which cost 130 guineas, had a top speed governed to 18 mph and it returned 37 miles to each gallon

Right: the Earl of Ranfurly's idea of what a motorised Hansom car should be; note the odd position of the driver

Far right: a four-cylinder 18 hp prototype of 1905; this was the first car to feature the unique fluting on the Vauxhall bonnet; seated in the rear of the car is W. G. Gardner who, at that time, was joint managing director of Vauxhall

The year of the big move to Luton naturally cramped manufacture—only a score of cars were produced. Some were attempts to produce a horseless version of a hansom cab, with the driver perched high up at the back where coachmen sat. This design, suggested by the Earl of Ranfurly, was backward-looking and quite against the engineering trends of the day which were establishing the car as an object in its own right, and not simply a different way of propelling a carriage. Vauxhall spotted this immediately, and at the London Motor Show in November 1905—despite the upheaval of the move to Luton—were able to show to the public a T-head four-cylinder 18 hp 3.3-litre car with a live rear axle and comparatively generous four-seater bodywork. The radiator was squarer, and the fluting along the top edges was now a string styling point. It was to remain until 1959, when it fell into disuse, and to reappear in 1972. Also in 1905, Vauxhall made their first move into competition, putting a works three-cylinder 3.3-litre car with overdrive gearbox into the Tourist Trophy.

The next step in the shaping of the company into a form which was to allow it to become one of Britain's 'Big Four' was the formation, in 1907, of Vauxhall Motors Ltd as a separate car-making concern. Marine engineering continued alongside the young car company until 1914, when the needs of the first fully mechanised war caused Vauxhall to concentrate on motor vehicles.

1907 saw the development of a smaller T-head car, the 12/16, which had shaft-drive and also of a design which came to be recognised as one of the classics of the decade: the Pomeroy-designed L-head 20 with a four-cylinder engine with five-bearing crankshaft and monobloc construction. The car leap to instant prominence, for in the 1908 RAC and Scottish Reliability Trials it became the first car in the world ever to complete 2000 miles without an involuntary stop. Variants on this chassis included an open-backed pickup design which Vauxhall historians like to think of as the firm's very first estate car.

Production during 1909 jumped to 195 cars, and included what was known at the time as a semi-racer, a 16 hp four-cylinder car with two seats, although some examples had a tiny extra seat behind: the firm's first sports model, perhaps, with a two-plus-one variant. At £350, it was expensive. Meanwhile, the firm was using competition to build its reputation further, a torpedo-shaped special called the KN registering quick times at Brooklands.

At Brooklands the following year, in fact, one of the 20 hp Vauxhalls became the first of its type to exceed 100 mph. No less significant in 1910, however, was designer Laurence Pomeroy's work on a prototype which was to result in the famous three-litre C-Type, named Prince Henry after winning the 1910 trials in Germany which carried that Prussian prince's name. This fast and elegant 19.9 hp model quickly grew up into a four-litre 22.5 hp capable of 75 mph. Its V-nose and cycle-type wheels became a familiar sight wherever trials and hill-climb enthusiasts met and, although in 1911 the chassis alone cost £485 (by 1915 the effects of wartime on materials prices had pushed this up to £565), there were plenty of buyers. Export markets

Below: this pick-up was built *circa* 1909

Below right: the 1908 Vauxhall 2000 miles trial team; the car on the left was the first ever to run for 2000 miles non-stop

Left: the C-type 'Prince Henry' of 1913; this car, which was very successful in competition, had a 22.5 hp engine

Below: a 25 hp of 1914; this Vauxhall was extremely popular with the army during World War I

Bottom: a 1920 E-Type 4½-litre car, with Wensum bodywork

this time included Russia, whose royal family had a distinct preference for the Luton product, and ordered several special cars. During this period, Vauxhall maintained a small workshop in Moscow staffed by British fitters, and there was a lavish Vauxhall catalogue printed in Russian.

A Linley pre-selector gearbox was quoted as a Vauxhall option in 1911, the year the firm started racing in earnest. Cars were entered for the Coupe de l'Auto voiturette races of 1911, 1912 and 1913, and these were followed by twin-overhead-camshaft designs in 1914 for the French Grand Prix and the Tourist Trophy. The 4.5-litre engines of the Grand Prix cars developed 130 bhp.

During this period, Vauxhall's bread-and-butter car was a smaller and more stolid A-type version of the Prince Henry design, joined in 1913 by a D-type with four-litre engine and even closer affinity to the Prince Henry sporting car. Small numbers of a B-type car with formal carriage-related bodywork and a six-cylinder unit, its cylinders cast in threes, were also manufactured.

1913 saw the advent of the most famous Vauxhall of all time—the 30/98, built in various forms until 1926, although only thirteen were made before the outbreak of World War I; the model designation of this car is unknown even to Vauxhall. In competition form its 4.5-litre engine put out 23.8 hp. In 1915, it was listed at £925. After 1919, it could cost up to £1950, depending on bodywork, although the post-war E-type version of it boasted full electrical equipment. Between 1920 and 1923, this model scored 75 firsts in hill-climb and track events including Shelsley Walsh and Brooklands. Sporting drivers and touring drivers alike loved the 30/98's combination of great flexibility and 80 mph-plus performance. For this, they usually forgave its barely adequate brakes.

During World War I, Vauxhall made D-type cars at the rate of eight a week for the fighting services, and a total of nearly 2000 cars were built during hostilities for the War Office. Vauxhall staff cars were used on all fronts; a Vauxhall 25 hp car took King George V to Vimy Ridge across the Flanders mud. Another carried General Allenby on his victorious entry into Jerusalem, and another made two trips from Salonika to Santa Quaranta on the Adriatic over four mountain ranges in Greece and Albania.

Yet another Vauxhall 25 was the first car to cross the River Rhine into Germany after the 1918 Armistice.

become the LM type, and a Wilson preselector gearbox was later offered as an option. The 30/98 survived into 1927, acquiring hydraulic brakes in the meantime, although only about 600 of the E and OE versions of this model were built in this late period, and sixty per cent of these were exported to Australia. The firm even introduced a new S-type luxury car, the 'Silent 80' with a 23 hp 3.9-litre six-cylinder single-sleeve-valve engine and hydraulic brakes, priced at £1250.

However, General Motors were after volume, and a change of emphasis was being programmed. The first product of the new situation came in 1928 with the 20/60, an overhead-valve six-cylinder car with coil ignition, central gear change and four forward speeds. It was variously offered with touring and coupé bodies, the latter introducing to the British scene the American-style of fixed-head box-top two-seater coupé with large fully upholstered dickey seat. Several independent coachbuilders used the R-type chassis, but in factory-built form the car came complete for only £475—*only*, that is, in previous Vauxhall terms.

The R-type increased in capacity, ending its pro-

And in Cairo, during the war, the Australian driver of a military Vauxhall 25 challenged a British officer who claimed to have the fastest car in Egypt—a non-British 35 hp car. Over a three-mile run from a standing start, the Vauxhall took 3 minutes 2.25 seconds—13.5 seconds faster than its bigger rival.

In 1922, a new 23/60 was developed from the 25 model, and it shared many components with the 30/98. Its four-cylinder engine was Vauxhall's first overhead-valve unit. It was available with a variety of bodies—open tourer, saloon and limousine—and remained in production for four years. Its average price was £895.

There was also a 14/40, aimed at the lower end of the market, and Vauxhall's first diversion towards the popular end of motoring. This model, known also as the M-type, had a 2.3-litre engine (quite small for the time), with detachable head, a three-speed unit gearbox in place of the four-speed separate type usual on large cars (although fur speeds came in in 1925), single-plate clutch, and all brakes on the rear wheels, supplanting a foot transmission brake. Price of the 14/40 M type was £750—there was still a very long way to go before the man in the street could begin to aspire to a Vauxhall.

The last serious competition Vauxhalls, before the firm withdrew from racing in 1923 (having chalked up 75 wins, 52 seconds, 35 thirds and fourteen best times in international, club and trial events and hill-climbs in the last three years of endeavour), were a team of three-litre twin-overhead-camshaft cars for the 1922 Tourist Trophy. They produced 110 bhp and had air-pressure-operated brakes, but even so managed no more than third place.

Both the D and E-Types acquired overhead valves in 1922, and as a result the E-type became known as the OE, with a 4.2-litre engine producing 120 bhp. The following year it acquired four-wheel brakes, but still Vauxhalls were not noted for their stopping capacity.

By 1924, Vauxhall was selling 1400 cars a year, but its financial position was still not strong, and when American giant General Motors went shopping in Britain for manufacturing facilities, both parties were not slow to see the advantages to themselves and each other in an arrangement. In 1925, General Motors acquired the ordinary shares of Vauxhall Motors Limited, the firm founded in 1907.

The firm continued for a few years to make the large and expensive cars for which it was known. The M-type 14/40 acquired front-wheel brakes in 1924 to

Top: the 1914 Isle of Man TT car which featured a 3.3-litre engine; in the race, the cars were unsuccessful, but were used at Brooklands after the war where they scored a few victories

Above: a Grosvenor-bodied M-type 14/40 of 1925, complete with popular Dickey seat

duction run in 1932 as the 3.3-litre T80 model. Meanwhile, the firm had really got to grips with the development and production of an inexpensive car, and in 1931 the first genuinely popular Vauxhall appeared— the Cadet, a two-litre six-cylinder offered in 17 hp form at £280 and as a 26 hp version at £295. In the same year, the firm took another significant step with the introduction under the Bedford badge of a small thirty cwt commercial vehicle, followed almost immediately by two and three-ton trucks, a twelve-seater bus chassis and a twelve cwt van. So successful were these Chevrolet-based introductions that in 1932, only a year later, more than 10,000 Bedfords were sold and, in 1932 alone, 6300 Bedfords were shipped abroad. This was GM's intended volume production with a vengeance, and the commercial-vehicle operation was to sustain the car side time and again in the future.

In the early 1930s, Vauxhall cars were doing well in their own right. In 1932, the Cadet became the first British car to fit a synchromesh gearbox, pre-dating even Rolls-Royce if only by a matter of a few months. the following year, the small-horsepower scene was added to with the Light Six A-type, again with an engine option—12 hp at £195 or 14 hp at £215; the latter proved to be the more popular. On announcement day, 250 Light Sixes were collected from the factory by Vauxhall dealers, which was an unprecedented achievement at the time, and reflected the efficiency which GM influence had clearly brought. In

Right: the 23 hp six-cylinder 'Silent 80' of 1931; again, this car features Grosvenor coachwork

Below: the Cadet, introduced in 1930, was the first car to be seen after the Vauxhall/General Motors link; it featured an engine of either 17 or 26 hp

1933, up to forty per cent of all 14 hp new-car registrations in Britain were of the Vauxhall Light Six. These cars remained in production until 1935, acquiring a number of refinements.

In 1934, two bigger sixes joined the Vauxhall range, the 2.4-litre BY of 20 hp and the 3.2 litre BX of 26 hp. These cars, which cost as little as £325, had Fisher no-draught ventilation and four forward speeds, and became very familiar as taxis and limousines through the 1930s, although they ceased production in 1936, by which time Vauxhall had nearly 8000 people on the payroll and was producing more than 50,000 vehicles of different sorts every year.

With this new volume prosperity came a lively model programme. 1935 saw a 14 hp DX and a 12 hp DY, these cars introducing independent front suspension (General Motors' knee-action) for the first time in the popular sector; the DY saloon sold from £205, and continued in production until 1938. A G-type 25 hp 3.2-litre model, large and comfortable and very American in appearance, appeared in 1936; long and short-wheelbase variants were produced between 1936 and 1939. This car would reach 80 mph but returned 20 mpg in normal driving conditions, and its £330 price included heater, fog lamp and a reversing light. The old radiators were giving way to stylised grilles during this period, and the now pear-shaped headlamps were attached to the shell. The Vauxhall flutes were still a strong styling feature.

In 1937, Vauxhall returned to the 10 hp class with

Below: seen on 5 June 1939 was this Grosvenor-bodied 25 hp drophead coupé

the very popular H-type. This 1.2-litre Ten with a three-speed gearbox had the distinction of being the first British car produced on the principle of integral construction—the body panels themselves forming a stiff shell instead of being mounted on the traditional chassis—and, although it was one of the most advanced small saloons of its day, the H-type was priced at only £158. Its 40 mpg was a further attraction to the growing numbers of people who were entering motoring with some financial trepidation. A coupé version with a separate chassis followed, and in 1938 came the I-type six-window saloon with 12 hp engine. This was later to be absorbed by the H-type when it adopted the 12 hp unit.

In 1938, Vauxhall launched an important new car, the J-type 14 hp with smooth six-cylinder 1781 cc engine giving an easy 30 mpg and a top speed of 70 mph. Its features included an adjustable steering column, no-draught ventilation, double-acting shock-absorbers, hydraulic brakes, adjustable foot-rests and seat armrests. In 1939, the price was a keen £220, and this provoked lively initial sales; production of the J-type was picked up after World War II.

Very soon after the declaration of hostilities, the Vauxhall factory was put on to war production. The 12,000 employees produced a large variety of war material. These included five million jerrycans, 250,000 Bedford trucks for the armed services, six-pounder armour-piercing shells, four-million venturi tubes for rocket launchers and, towards the end of the war, 95 per cent of the engines for the first dozen jet-aircraft produced in Britain.

Vauxhall's most impressive war effort, perhaps, was the Churchill tank—the successful 38-ton machine powered by a 375 bhp twelve-cylinder petrol engine—which went from drawing board to final production in one year, a fantastic achievement even in wartime. Nearly 5650 Churchills were produced, some at other factories which took parts from Luton.

At the end of the war, the works had half-a-dozen prototypes of the Churchill successor under test, and also a three-quarter-track military vehicle based on a captured German vehicle.

All this activity attracted a visit from the Luftwaffe on 30 August 1940, with 39 being killed in the raid and forty seriously injured. Despite heavy damage, the factory was in full swing again within six days. Though the German airforce did not raid Vauxhall again, they knew where it was all right: an executive of Opel, now Vauxhall's partner in the General Motors European operation, recently admitted to having been a Luftwaffe pilot during the war, and revealed that, although the Luton factory was heavily camouflaged (the green wartime paint is still discernible on the main administration block overlooking the main site), a graveyard on the other side of the hill was overlooked, and the pattern of white stones provided a positive landmark for the German pilots even at night, as they winged their way across that part of the Midlands!

With the resumption of civilian-vehicle manufacture in 1946, the immediate pre-war models went back into production, all of them of unitary construction with the exception of certain export versions which continued until 1954. Revised editions of the 10, 12 and 14 hp H and J-type models of 1939/40 were offered, although the arrival of the flat-rate car-tax

cal in appearance to the six-cylinder model, it offered 35 mpg. Both had steering-column gearchange, the first Vauxhalls to feature this American-style shift.

With the post-war boom producing a clamour for all motor products, Vauxhall clearly needed to expand its production facilities, and in 1948 work began on a large new factory at Luton—a £14 million project on a 19½-acre site within the original factory boundary. Within two years, there emerged from this new plant a completely new range of seven-ton forward-control Bedford trucks, including a chassis for a 39-seater bus. Tractor units for articulated vehicles followed, and the range extended into the ten-ton payload bracket.

The L-type cars remained in production until mid 1951, when they were replaced by the E-type, although the names were retained. The 2.2-litre six-cylinder Velox and the 1.5-four-cylinder Wyvern introduced the hypoid-bevel rear axle, curved windscreen and side-opening bonnets to Vauxhall. The following year a new square engine was introduced, in 2262 cc form in the Velox and 1507 cc for the Wyvern. In 1953, Golden Jubilee year for Vauxhall cars, the Velox was offered with an optional high-compression cylinder head giving 7.6:1, and the following year a luxurious version of the six-cylinder Velox, the Cresta, was added to the range.

Detail styling changes and improvement to the mechanical specifications were regularly brought in on this range, but the basic body shape remained until 1957, although changes were being introduced—a new grille was brought in for 1956—right to the end. In all, 341,626 of the E-type cars were made, and in 1963 this range took Vauxhall past the 100,000 a year production rate and also past the total production mark of one million vehicles.

Below: after World War II, production resumed with cars like this 14 hp J-Type, left, and the 10 hp H-Type

Bottom: the first new cars after the war were the L-Type Velox and Wyvern; this is the 2¼-litre six-cylinder Velox, which had a top speed of 75 mph

system led to the dropping of the 10 hp car from September 1947. The remaining 12 gave 33–36 mpg and reached 65 mph, while the 14 reached 70 mph and averaged 25–28 mpg. Vauxhall car production in 1947 exceeded 30,300 and total Bedford truck production exceeded 500,000—the first British commercial-vehicle manufacturer to pass this point. The range now grew and included light vans as well as a 26-seater bus chassis.

The first new Vauxhall cars of the post-war era appeared in 1948—the L-type Velox and Wyvern, a complete breakaway from pre-war styling, and showing a strong trans-Atlantic influence in the frontal treatment, which included headlamps mounted in the wings. The 75 mph Velox had a 54 bhp 2.3-litre six-cylinder unit, while the Wyvern utilised the 35 bhp 1.4-litre engine of the old 12 model. In this car, identi-

In 1952, the Vauxhall factory at Luton had spread over 84 acres of floor space, and more than 12,000 people were employed there. However, the bustling expansion programme meant that even this big complex was not big enough, and 1953 saw the start of the company's most ambitious building project. £36 million was allocated to raise the company's production capacity to 250,000 units a year. To do this it was necessary to separate the car and commercial-vehicle production.

A complete new truck factory was started at Dunstable, six miles away, while a 36-acre addition to the car facility was planned at Luton. By 1955, the Dunstable factory was producing trucks powered by Bedford's own diesels, and in that year more Bedfords were made—67,773—than any other British make. The record Vauxhall/Bedford sales total was 142,149.

In February 1957, the new Luton car plant was ready to send out its first car, a brand new Victor F-type with Chevrolet-style wrap-round windscreen, stylised Vauxhall fluting bursting like a long cut down each flank, and an overall appearance that had a lot of critics. The Victor had a 1.5-litre four-cylinder engine and three-speed all-synchromesh gearbox, and a price tag of £729; there was also a more expensive Victor Super version. The car quickly became Britain's top export car, and in 1957 Vauxhall sold a record 114,177 vehicles. The following year saw a two-pedal variant with Newtondrive clutch-less gear change, and the Victor series passed the 100,000 mark in 1958, fifteen months after introduction, and this same year saw the 250,000 a year Vauxhall/Bedford production target reached, only two years after the £36 million expansion programme had been started.

Over the next two years, further extensions were

Above: the updated Velox of 1952

Below: nearly four hundred 745 F-Type built between 1957 and 1961. This is a 1961 Deluxe

Bottom: the 2.6-litre Cresta of 1961

made at Luton and Dunstable to bring total capacity to 300,000 a year. In 1959, the Victor went into Series 2 with cleaner, simpler styling, and a De Luxe version was offered. Meanwhile, two new six-cylinder cars had been introduced in 1957, the PA Velox and the Cresta, with 2.2-litre oversquare engines. In 1959, overdrive came in as an option on the sixes, with Hydramatic automatic transmission in 1960, when the engine capacity was raised to 2.5-litres. A new one-piece rear window with wrap-round corners and a more oval grille were also introduced, and Vauxhall collaborated with Friary Motors to produce the Friary Estate version of the Velox and Cresta. Vauxhall's two-millionth vehicle was a PA Cresta produced in February 1959. Disc front brakes and separate front seats joined the options in 1961. In March 1962, the warranty on all Vauxhall cars went up from six to twelve months.

The 1962 Victor FB, styled after consultation with a sculptor, was a better-looking car that dropped the traditional Vauxhall fluting altogether. The power unit was a 56 bhp 1508 cc four-cylinder engine, and four models were offered—standard, super, de luxe and estate. A more powerful version, the VX 4/90, had a twin-carburettor engine with a compression ratio of 9.3:1 giving 81.6 bhp—44 per cent more output than the standard engine. Disc brakes were fitted to all four wheels of this model.

In 1963, the Victor engine size was raised to 1594 cc, with a 69 bhp power output and an 8.5:1 compression ratio. The VX 4/90 version now gave 85.5 bhp and a top speed of over 90 mph. Disc brakes were standard on this version, and optional on other Victors. In this year, restyled Velox and Cresta models reached the showrooms, with a strong family resemblance. The 2.5-litre six-cylinder engine from the PA models was continued in this PB series. A three-speed column-change gearbox was standard, with overdrive and Hydramatic transmission as options. Disc front brakes were standard.

Martin Walter estate versions of both sixes were introduced in 1963, with lower final-drive ratios. 1964 saw a substantial change in the engine compartment with the appearance of a new 3.3-litre power unit. Four-speed floor-mounted gearchange and individual front seats were among the options. In this same year, Vauxhall reached new sales heights with 342,873 cars and commercial vehicles sold. This had only been possible because of further expansion.

By 1960, the management foresaw a rising home and foreign demand, and a need for further production

was a two-litre overhead-cam unit borrowed from the newly developed Victor 2000 and, with twin-carburettors, it gave 112 bhp. Many safety features, large disc brakes, full instrumentation, a matt black bonnet with twin air scoops and special wheels characterised this powerful version.

In the same year, two Viva estates and two saloons were offered with a 1600 cc overhead-camshaft engine of 83 bhp, while a four-door Viva body was added a few months later; the model also acquired an energy-absorbing steering column.

In 1968, British sales of Vivas reached over 103,000 and gave the model the bigger market share of any Vauxhall ever. Vauxhall was now offering no fewer

facilities if Vauxhall and Bedford were going to remain among the leading vehicle producers. In 1961, the biggest and most costly expansion programme in the firm's history began.

Because of government policy, it was not possible to expand further in the Luton and Dunstable area, so the company decided on a site at Ellesmere Port, Cheshire, in the growing Merseyside development area. On a 395-acre site near the river, a three-phase factory project got under way. The total cost was to be £68 million, and the result was a new self-contained plant capable of producing 176,000 cars a year with a labour force of around 12,000. Production of mechanical components began there in November 1963, and the assembly of a new small car, the Viva, was begun in June 1964.

The two-door Viva had a 1057cc engine, and was very close in concept and design to the Kadett model produced by Opel, General Motors' German subsidiary. The HA Viva, introduced at £566, was the first car in Britain to be given an acrylic-laquer finish. This model, which ran for three years, had a curious fold-over finish to the rear wings which was not much liked by critics, but within a year of production opening up in Cheshire the 100,000th Viva had been produced.

In the same year, the Victor went into 101 form, Vauxhall having produced 328,642 FB Victors. The 101 FC series Victors were offered in three saloon forms, two estates and the VX 4/90 sporting package. They featured curved windows for the first time, pioneering them in this class of car in Britain, and making something of a stride in the better utilisation of the space within the shell. It did not take other car designers long to follow these features.

The 101 series inherited the 1594cc engine of the previous Victor. In 1965, two new options were introduced—a limited-slip differential and Powerglide automatic transmission; the limited-slip differential became standard on the VX 4/90 in 1966. The 101 models were superceded by the FD Victors in 1967.

Meanwhile, the Viva series had been developing. While this car had taken Vauxhall back into the one-litre class with some degree of emphasis on economy, 1965 saw an SL version and a '90' model— De Luxe 90 and SL 90 with 60 bhp and a 9:1 compression ratio. There were now five Viva models and, within 27 months, of introduction the model had passed the quarter-million mark. By the time the HA Vivas made way for the HB models, in March 1966, 307,738 had been built.

The HB Vivas came in five versions. Engine size was up to 1159cc, and the body, just over six inches longer, was far more sleek. All-coil-suspension gave a much improved ride. The HB moved into a strongly sporty area with introduction in March 1968 of a GT version, the first Vauxhall to be so labelled. The engine

Top: a Martin Walter estate-car design on a Cresta; also available on a Velox base, the car had a luggage area of 41 cu ft

Above: the Viva was the Luton company's staple production car through the 1960s and '70s; this is a Deluxe four-door of 1975 in HC form

than 26 versions. By the time the Viva HB was superceded in October 1970, 556,752 had been built.

Vauxhall had, meanwhile, been active on the large-car front. The Cresta went into PC form in 1965 with two versions, standard and de luxe. The 3.3-litre engine, passed on from the previous car (the Velox version did not survive the model change), put out 140bhp and gave the car a comfortable 100mph top speed. Three-speed column change with or without overdrive, four-speed floor change, and Powerglide automatic transmission were offered.

1966 saw a super-luxury version of the Cresta, the Viscount, with power steering, electric windows, Powerglide transmission, and traditional English leather and walnut trim. The Viscount also set a trend for black vinyl as a roof finish. The Cresta and Viscount lasted until 1972, and were not replaced by comparable cars, Vauxhall then concentrating lower down the market.

In 1967, Vauxhall changed the Victor for an FD model with a choice of 1599cc and 1975cc overhead-camshaft (by toothed belt, then a significant innovation), five-bearing-crankshaft four-cylinder engines. These units were the ones to be offered in the performance versions of the Viva HB in 1968. The Victor and Victor 2000 had an energy-absorbing steering column, rack-and-pinion steering, all-coil suspension and transmission was either three-speed column change, four-speed floor shift or Borg Warner automatic. Soon after its launching, the Victor 2000 was awarded the Don Safety Trophy (now recognised as the world's premier car safety award) as the vehicle

Above: the FE Victor 2300 of 1975

Above right: the top of the range car in 1975 was this Ventora, which was powered by a 3.3-litre straight-six engine

Right: the Viva grew in engine size from just over 1100 cc to 2.3 litres. This is the 2300 two-door Magnum which uses a Viva shell

that most contributed to road safety in 1967.

The 3.3-litre six-cylinder engine made its way into the FD bodyshell in 1968 with the Ventora, which also made four-speed floor shift standard and offered considerable luxury. Three Victor FD estates appeared in 1968, too, the top version having the 3.3-litre engine. In 1969, the VX 4/90 badge reappeared on a twin-carburettor version of the Victor 2000 engine allied to a four-speed manual gearbox, full instrumentation, individually reclining front seats, disc brakes and sports wheels.

The FD Victors and derivatives gave way in 1971 to the FE models, with a chunky shape relating very closely to, and sharing many inner skin panels with, the comparable Opels. The engines were 1800 and 2300 cc overhead-camshaft four-cylinder units, while the Ventora continued to use the 3.3-litre six-cylinder engine. There were seven FE models which re-introduced the bonnet fluting disused after 1959.

The Viva story continued after 1970 with the introduction of the HC models. Two and four-door and estate bodies, all of entirely new design and again relating to Opel models in the same class, were powered on introduction by 1159 cc engines, with a 1600 cc overhead-camshaft option. General Motors' own automatic transmission was offered. In 1973, the engine line-up was revised with three new choices of 1256 cc, 1600 and 2300 cc. Meanwhile in 1971 a coupé version, the Firenza, was introduced, its shapely fixed head shell being based on the HC. Originally available with the 1159, 1600 and 2000 cc engine choices, it followed the Viva engine changes in 1973, and a

2300-engined Sport SL version with twin carburettors was introduced to the line.

Later in 1973, Vauxhall overhauled the whole Viva-Firenza range, retaining the Viva name for the 1256 cc saloon, renaming the 1800 and 2300 saloons, Magnums, coupés and estates and giving the Firenza name to a high-performance coupé with dramatic shovel-nosed styling which owed a great deal to competition experience gained by the semi-works-supported Dealer Team Vauxhall. Much of the engine development for this effort was the work of Vauxhall tuning specialist, Bill Blydenstein. DTV participation in circuit and rally events continue with considerable success.

1973 also saw the start of a new investment programme of £53 million for a new range of heavy trucks and the further development of new cars. Bedford vans took a record order—3200 HA models worth over £2 million for the Post Office.

Another new Vauxhall model was the Chevette, in basic and L form—a shapely hatchback tailgate coupé using the 1256 cc engine and rear-wheel drive train to far better effect than the Viva, and hailed as Vauxhall's best-ever car, although the Viva undersold it. The Chevette, with excellent handling and road-holding and a top speed of around 90-mph, was the first of a number of models from General Motors firms around the world sharing many common components.

Much of the development work for GM cars and trucks takes places at a £3.5 million 700-acre proving ground at Millbrook, eighteen miles from Luton, completed in 1971 by Vauxhall. It is claimed to be the most advanced vehicle proving ground in Europe. EF

Left: a 1912 Vauxhall 35 hp model; built on a B12 chassis, and powered by a six-cylinder engine, it was commissioned by the Russian Royal Family

Below: the first Vauxhall model, the single-cylinder runabout of 1904

Left: the C-type Vauxhall of 1911; known as the 'Prince Henry', it was powered by a four-cylinder, 3969 cc, 75 bhp engine. When new, these machines sold for £485

Below: a 30/98 Vauxhall tourer of 1922; built from 1922 until 1928, these machines were fitted with four-cylinder, overhead valve engines of 4224 cc, which produced 112 bhp at 3400 rpm

The Vauxhall Firenza was first introduced at the 1973 London Motor Show, but was not put on sale until a year later, and even then in limited numbers.

There may be some confusion over the cars name: the ordinary coupé Vivas were once called Firenzas, and were available with 1256, 1759 and 2279 cc engines. Then, the small-engined car was dropped and the range was renamed Magnum and also included the larger-engined (1759 and 2279 cc) saloons and estates. So, by this time, there was no model called the Firenza. That was until the introduction of the new top of the range coupé that had a more powerful engine and better aero-dynamics than its sisters.

The Firenza's power unit is of the same capacity as the overhead-camshaft 2300 Magnum, but it has a higher compression ratio, bigger valves, and hand-finished ports and combustion chambers. A ZF

five-speed gearbox transmits the car's 131 bhp and 142 lb ft of torque to the rear wheels. The price of the gearbox alone costs well over £300.

Outwardly, the first thing one notices of the car is its 'droop snoot' shovel nose. This gives the car better air penetration than the other Vauxhalls and makes it stand out from the crowd. With good aerodynamics and a powerful engine, the car has a top speed of 122 mph and accelerates to 60 mph from rest in 8.0 secs. The car manages 22 miles to the gallon.

Finally, to make the Vauxhall a delightful driver's car, it has been given suspension that makes for clean, easy handling, and fat tyres that grip the road well. On the safety side, it has Avon Safety rims designed into the light-alloy wheels.

ENGINE Front-mounted, water-cooled straight-four. 97.5 mm (3.84 in) bore × 76.2 mm (3 in)

stroke = 2279 cc (139.1 cu in). Maximum power (DIN) 131 bhp at 5500 rpm; maximum torque (DIN) 142 lb ft at 3600 rpm. Cast-iron cylinder block and head. Compression ratio 9.2:1. 5 main bearings. 2 valves per cylinder operated, direct, by a belt-driven overhead cam-shaft. 2 Zenith-Stromberg 175 CD-2SE semi-downdraught single-barrel carburettors.

TRANSMISSION Single-dry-plate clutch and five-speed manual ZF gearbox. Ratios, 1st 2.990, 2nd 1.760, 3rd 1.300, 4th 1, 5th 0.870, rev 3.670:1. Hypoid-bevel final drive. Ratio, 3.700.

CHASSIS Integral.

SUSPENSION Front—independent by wishbones, lower trailing links, coil springs, an anti-roll bar and telescopic dampers, rear—non-independent by a rigid axle, lower trailing arms, upper oblique torque arms, coil

springs and telescopic dampers.

STEERING Rack and pinion. Turns from lock to lock 3.16.

BRAKES Servo-assisted front discs and rear drums.

WHEELS 6 in × 13 in light-alloy, with Avon Safety Wheel rims.

TYRES 185/70 HR × 13.

DIMENSIONS AND WEIGHT Wheelbase 97.40 in; track—front 52.90 in, rear—53 in; length 169.40 in; width 64.70 in; height 51.90 in; ground clearance 5.25 in; dry weight 2178 lb; turning circle between walls 34 ft; fuel tank capacity 12 gals.

BODY 2-door, 4-seater coupé.

PERFORMANCE Maximum speed 122 mph. Acceleration 0–60 mph 8.0 secs. Fuel consumption approximately 22 mpg.

CHEVETTE

When the Vauxhall Chevette was introduced in March 1975, it arrived at just the right time for the public and Luton company, alike.

With petrol prices soaring, and the everyday motorist's priorities moving away from performance toward economy, the little 1256 cc-engined, three-door family car seemed to fit the bill perfectly.

The car's engine is the venerable four-cylinder, overhead-valve, cast-iron unit that powers the larger, although cheaper, Viva. In Chevette form, it produces 58.5 bhp and 68 lb ft of torque. The transmission, a four-speed manual unit, is the same as that available in the Vauxhall Viva.

The Chevette suspension is conventional of the independent front, rigid rear type, by upper wishbones, lower transverse arms, brake reaction rods, coil springs, telescopic dampers and an anti-roll bar, forwards,

and a live axle, located by located by trailing arms, Panhard rod and torque tube, telescopic dampers and an anti-roll bar, aft. In the roadholding and handling departments, the car's extremely good performance is unconventional compared with many other front-engined, and rear-wheel-driven saloons. In fact, it has been said of the car that it is like a family-size go-kart.

Braking is taken care of by servo-assisted front discs and rear drums, whilst steering is by rack and pinion, with 3.8 turns from lock to lock.

The Chevette has a third rear door, and a bench rear seat that folds down all of which makes the automobile especially suitable and convenient for carrying bulky and otherwise awkward parcels and bundles.

ENGINE Front-mounted, water-cooled straight-four. 80.97 mm (3.188 in) bore × 60.96 mm

(2.400 in) stroke = 1256 cc (76.6 cu in). Maximum power (DIN) 58.5 bhp at 5600 rpm; maximum torque (DIN) 68 lb ft at 2600 rpm. Cast-iron cylinder block and head. Compression ratio 9.2:1. 3 main bearings. 2 valves per cylinder operated, via pushrods and rockers, by a single camshaft, side. 1 Zenith-Stromberg 150CDS (E) V side-draught single-barrel carburettor.

TRANSMISSION Single-dry-plate clutch and four-speed manual gearbox. Ratios, 1st 3.460, 2nd 2.213, 3rd 1.404, 4th 1, rev 3.707:1. Hypoid-bevel final drive. Ratio 4.111:1.

CHASSIS Integral.

SUSPENSION Front—independent by upper wishbones, lower transverse arms, brake reaction rods, coil springs, telescopic dampers and an anti-roll bar, rear—non-independent by a

rigid axle, located by two trailing arms, Panhard rod and torque tube, coil springs and telescopic dampers.

STEERING Rack and pinion. Turns from lock to lock 3.8.

BRAKES Servo-assisted front discs and rear drums.

WHEELS 13 in × 5 in steel.

TYRES 155SR × 13.

DIMENSIONS AND WEIGHT Wheelbase 94.3 in; track—front and rear 51.3 in; length 155.3 in; width 62.3 in; height 52 in; ground clearance 5.3 in; dry weight 1825 lb; turning circle between walls 28 ft; fuel tank capacity 8 gals.

BODY 3-door, 4–5-seater saloon.

PERFORMANCE Maximum speed 90 mph. Acceleration 0–60 mph 15 secs. Fuel consumption approximately 30 mpg.

WARM IN WINTER, COOL IN SUMMER

In days gone by, the car's ventilation was provided by the wind as it whistled through the cars' bodies; nowadays, there is much more to it

IN THE DAWN of the motoring era, cars could be described as having total ventilation, since they had open bodies without even a windscreen between the occupants and the elements. Driving was essentially an open-air pursuit, and those who indulged in it had to dress themselves suitably or suffer the consequences. Gradually though, as designers became more competent and purchasers more demanding, 'sophistication' began to creep in. First, the windscreen to blunt the force of wind and rain, then some sort of a hood which could be erected to keep the worst of the rain off the people inside.

The next milestone was the inception of the enclosed coach-built body. Although such bodies were very much in the minority until perhaps the late 1920s, they did offer considerably better protection to the occupants than open ones, even though the makers of the latter had by then adopted celluloid 'side curtains'; these clipped into the top of the doors, or the rim of the body sides, and were supposed to fill the gaps between these and the hood when this was unfurled. Such was the flexibility, and the amount of flapping that went on, however, that what one might call natural ventilation was still of a high order. It was assisted, particularly in the case of the front compartment of a four-seater, by various holes in the floor, through which protruded such items as the pedals and steering column. The expression 'cold feet' had a very real meaning to the winter driver of those days!

When the closed car began to become the predominant type around 1930, the motorist found himself faced with a new problem—that of 'fug'. To prevent the car interior from becoming unbearably stuffy in hot weather, and the window glass from misting-up when it was cold or wet, the occupants had only one course open to them: they had to open something to get a circulation of air. An open window and/or the upper half of the windscreen (at that time a two-piece horizontally divided screen, was quite common) was effective but, since it gave rise to draughts and let in rain, it could hardly be regarded as ideal. Various improvements were therefore evolved during the 1930s. They included opening quarter-lights on the side windows and louvres above opening panels; these louvres enabled the windows to be opened a little without the entry of rain, and they also improved the draught situation, but only so long as some overlap was maintained with the main glass.

Heaters began to be fitted to American cars in the late 1930s, but they did not appear on ordinary cars this side of the Atlantic until the advent of the first generation of genuinely post-war models. Even then they were rather primitive, being of the recirculatory type which means that they merely draw in the air already in the body, heat it and push it out again by means of an electric fan. Because of the amount of water vapour breathed out by the occupants, and the fact that in winter the glass was cold outside and the

air warm inside, cars with recirculatory heaters were very prone to misting-up in these circumstances unless some window opening was used to provide ventilation for the interior of the automobile.

Following on from the thinking behind the louvres mentioned earlier, various accessory companies in the 1950s brought out deflectors of moulded transparent plastics material. These clipped into the front corner of the driver's window frame and were so shaped that, in theory at least, the window could be opened quite a way without draughts. In practice, too, some of these devices were reasonably effective, not only at blocking draughts but even more so at providing an extractor action for stale air within the car.

The next step forward on the manufacturing front was the collaboration of the car and heater manufacturers to produce fresh-air systems. As the term indicates, these took in air from outside the car, either from alongside the radiator (where they tended to ingest the exhaust fumes of other vehicles also) or from just in front of the windscreen. The air entered the body by ram effect, caused by the motion of the vehicle, but fan assistance was available for low-speed driving and to help clear misted windows. This arrangement had obvious advantages over the recirculatory one but had one major drawback: there is a limit to the amount of fresh air that can be pushed into the car, even by a fan, unless the stale air can find its way out at the same time. The situation was not helped either by the steady improvement in door

Below: the interior of this Fiat 130 is well equipped to keep both driver and passenger happy, on the left, there is a face-level fresh-air vent, while there are warm-air vents on the centre of the dashboard and on the transmission tunnel by the driver's feet. With this system, the driver can have cool air blowing on his face (to help keep him alert on motorways, for instance), whilst still keeping his body warm

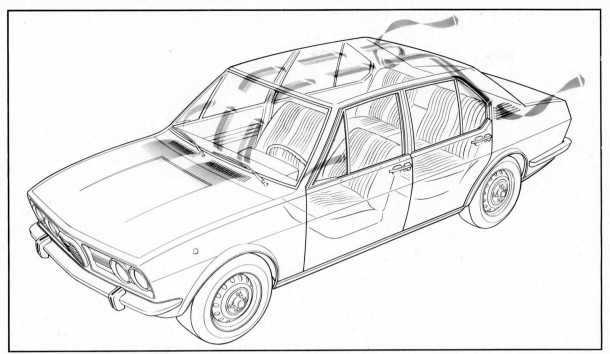

Left: this diagram of
an Alfetta shows how
the air is channeled
through the car; cool air
enters at the front and
is split up into two
currents, see *bottom*;
it flows through the
car and escapes by
extractors at the rear,
along with any fumes

Below: the airflow
inside the NSU Ro80.
Note, that this car
has extractors by the
rear seats

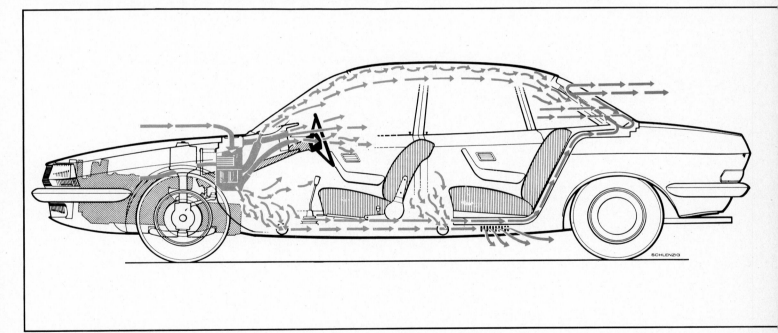

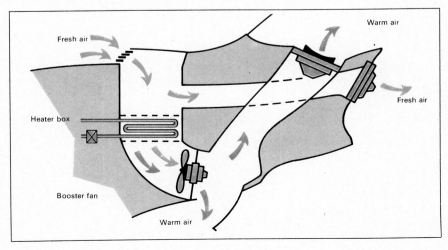

sealing which reduced the 'leakage' extraction that
had taken place earlier. Ducting led from the heater to
the body interior and the windscreen, as in the case of
some recirculatory systems.

Various improvements were made on the fresh-air
theme during the late 1950s and early 1960s, especially
on the more expensive cars. The real breakthrough in
Britain, however, came at the popular-price end of
the market when, in the autumn of 1964, Ford introduced their Aeroflow through-flow ventilation system
on the 1965 version of the Mark 1 Cortina. In this well
thought-out system, Ford really got down to funda-
mentals. Their starting point was the efficient *extraction* of stale air from the inside of the body, and to
achieve it they incorporated grille-covered outlets in
the rear quarter panels; these outlets were sited, as a
result of tests in the wind tunnel, in areas of low external aerodynamic pressure, to ensure that the air would

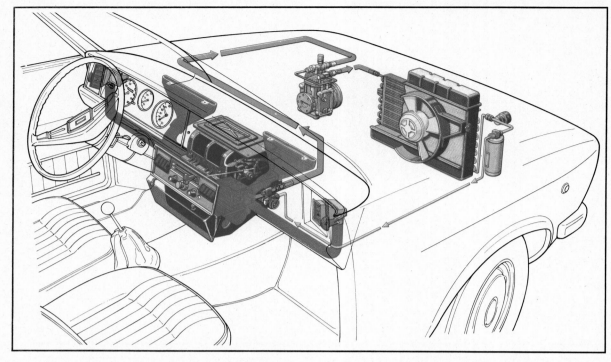

be drawn out of the car rather than pushed into it.

On the input side, too, Ford had something new to offer—'eyeball' adjustable vents, one at each end of the fascia to supplement the fresh-air feed to the heater (and thence of course to the body interior and the windscreen). These eyeballs were adjustable in two respects. First, they had four 'quantity' settings—off, low, high, and low but warmed by the heater; in all the 'on' positions, the supply could be boosted by the fan if required. Also, the eyeballs could be swivelled universally, enabling the flow to be directed at the front seat occupants or along the sides to help clear condensation from the windows in wet or cold weather. Yet another refinement was the incorporation of baffles over the extractors, on the inside of the quarters. These baffles ensured that the air could get to the outlets only from behind, so it had to flow over the rear window and hence assist in the demisting of this when necessary.

The Aeroflow system was so successful and widely acclaimed that virtually everyone else had to fall into line by evolving comparable through-flow ventilation layouts. At the time of writing, there are still one or two saloon cars that incorporate neither positive extraction nor fascia outlets, but their tendency to stuffiness and misting-up is so noticeably worse than that of their properly ventilated competitors that it seems incredible that they have survived so long and inevitable that they will eventually have to adopt a more efficient system.

Variations from the original Ford concept have been mainly in respect of the size, number and positioning of the fascia outlets and in the extraction arrangements. After the early Mark 2 Cortinas, Ford simplified their own layout by deleting the warmed-air facility on the eyeballs (a pity, in the opinion of many) and going from pull-push separate volume controls to rotary knobs in the middle of the outlets; these at least gave an infinitely variable setting range. For the Mark 1 Escort, a further simplification replaced eyeballs and screen-demisting slots by a pair of relatively large-diameter louvred outlets mounted medially on top of the fascia. These could be rotated to direct the flow from the louvres in the desired direction. Again, this

scheme was appreciably less effective than the original of 1965.

Some manufacturers did not favour eyeball outlets but, instead, developed grid-type ones in which both the vertical and horizontal vanes were pivoted and so could be inclined as desired for directing the flow. Certain higher-priced cars now even have a combination of grids or eyeballs at the ends of the facia and central outlets below it. Only the latter, usually, are in series with the fan and heater, the others being ram-fed with fresh air from outside. Normally, these ventilating means are designed into the automobile's body in conjunction with the conventional windscreen-clearing slots and heater outlets into the interior of the body.

Although the rear quarters remain the most favoured site for the extractors, other arrangements are used. For a start, most estate cars have no quarter panels, so their outlet grilles have to be in either the rear pillars or the body sides. Even in the latter case, though, the air is usually drawn from the body into the pillars to get a flow across the rear window. In other instances, the outgoing air flows through a grille in the rear parcel shelf and thence to atmosphere through a further grille in the boot decking, or even through the boot itself.

On quite a number of cars, there is still room for improvement on the extraction side because, as indicated earlier, the air cannot come in readily unless easy exit is provided as well. The need for facilitating the way out is witnessed on the models concerned by the significant improvement that occurs in both ventilation and heater output when a rear window (or maybe the sun-roof) is opened. The problem here may be simply inadequate size of the extractor passages and grilles, but there is always the possibility that the external pressure at the outlets is not low enough to induce a good flow. In this case, increasing the passage size would help, but would be less effective than resiting the outlets in an area where there is lower external air pressure. In spite of these particular criticism, there is no doubt that the general standard of ventilation on the ordinary car of today is vastly better than that of ten years ago.　　AB

OLD OLDER AND OLDEST

There is much popular confusion over 'what came first' in motoring: the veteran or the vintage. However, the answer is quite simple

VETERAN, EDWARDIAN, VINTAGE . . . that's the game of the name. And where old cars are concerned, these purely arbitrary divisions can make a considerable difference to the value of a vehicle, though recent years have brought a more fluid attitude to the situation, so that a car tends nowadays to be judged on its merits, not just on the accident of its date of original construction.

But it was all very precisely defined right at the beginning, for the first classification to be established was 'veteran', then and afterwards and now—*tunc et post et modo*—defined as having been built before

31 December, 1904, which was established half-a-century ago as the date on which motoring's infancy ended. Initially established as the qualifying date for the *Daily Sketch* 'Old Crock's Runs' of 1927–8–9, it was crystallised as the cut-on date for eligibility of membership of the Veteran Car Club when that body was founded in Brighton on 23 November, 1930, after the first RAC-organised Veteran Car Run, by S. C. H. Davis, Jackie Masters and John Wylie.

A better choice of date would have been the end of 1905, which would have neatly encompassed events such as the last Gordon Bennett race series: and indeed the Department of the Environment recognises all cars made before 31 December, 1905, as veterans able to take advantage of certain legal concessions, such as freedom from the obligation to fit such tiresome items as mudguards. But the date was fixed so long ago that it would be pointless to alter it now, when its main significance is to determine eligibility for the annual London–Brighton Commemoration Veteran Car Run, which always has an over-subscribed entry list anyway.

The Veteran Car Club, as befits the world's oldest antique car organisation, is the supreme arbiter on dating of early cars, and possession of a VCC Dating Certificate is virtually a *sine qua non* for any prospective entry in the Brighton Run. It was not always thus,

Above left: the very first London to Brighton run, in 1896; the sixty-odd mile event was to become the premier meeting for veteran cars

Above: the Veteran Car Club was founded on 23 November 1930; Jackie Masters was one of the founders

Left: a Vintage Sports Car Club meeting at Silverstone in 1961; here a group of cars in a Le Mans-type start, get somewhat entangled

This page, top: even when this picture was taken in the early part of the century, there were people restoring cars to their original condition. Here we see a couple of veteran cars. On the left is a City and Suburban electric, once the property of Queen Alexandra, and on the right is a Humberette

Centre: John Wylie, another of the founders of the Veteran Car Club

Below: a span of 23 years' racing is marked by these two Mercedes, of 1934 and 1914 'vintage' respectively

Opposite page, top: a 1900 Benz on the world-famous veteran car run from London to Brighton

Bottom: the scene on Brighton's promenade after the '68 event

however, and there are tales of a 1909 Humber—and perhaps even a post-1919 car!—being accepted as eligible for the 'Brighton' during the 1930s.

But these were small considerations beside the regrettable oversight which failed to make any provision for cars of the 1905–14 persuasion, which resulted in the destruction of a number of interesting and significant cars simply because there was no organisation catering for them.

The Veteran Car Club grew slowly during the 1930s—by 1939 there were around 250 members, owning some 150 cars—and during World War II, when emotive scrap drives of the 'saucepans for Spitfires' ilk were posing a far more positive threat to early cars than any amount of indifference, the Veteran Car Club at last widened its terms of reference to take in all cars made before 31 December, 1916 for all its events except the Brighton Run. This date was later extended to the end of 1918 to accommodate private cars produced overseas during the latter part of World War I.

But these cars—which became known conveniently, if not historically correctly, as Edwardians—had already found a champion, in the shape of the Vintage Sports Car Club, founded in 1934. Founded in protest at what were felt to be the rapidly declining standards of sports car design in the early 1930s, the VSCC (originally called the Veteran Sports Car Club, but renamed at the request of the Veteran Car Club) was originally intended for owners of pre-1931 light sports cars, but was very soon extended to cover any car, regardless of engine capacity, provided that it had been built at least five years before 1 January, 1935. Most of the early members owned cars such as 3-litre Bentleys, 30/98 Vauxhalls and 12/50 Alvis, but the oldest vehicle in the club at its inception was Lieutenant-Colonel J. Clutton's 16 hp Fafnir of 1910.

At their 1936 Annual General Meeting, the Vintage Sports Car Club approved a special class for cars built between 1905–15, feeling that many historic machines would otherwise be broken up because no club catered for them. And, defining the limit of what can strictly be called 'vintage', the VSCC decided to keep the range of eligible vehicles to pre-31 December 1930, and not advance the date every

year, as had been suggested. The 'start date' for vintage models was subsequently established as 1 January 1919. Thus three definite classes for antique vehicles were established:

Veteran	pre-1905
Edwardian	1905–1918
Vintage	1919–1930

Which left another problem: what about the many worthy vehicles built during the 1930s which conformed to the VSCC's ideas of excellence? At the VSCC General Meeting at Bagshot, Surrey, in September 1945, a fourth classification was agreed: Post-Vintage Thoroughbred 1931–1940.

This classification, however, had the drawback that it was based on arbitrary committee approval of the particular make or model.

But at the time it was thought to be vitally necessary to create a new class to ensure the continuity of membership—it was thought that the older cars would gradually wear out, and the club's *raison détre* be lost. They had not, of course, taken into account the virtual indestructibility of the average vintage car, which could motor on for years after its original life expectancy had expired. However, it did bring new blood into the club, and resulted in the preservation of some of the more interesting cars of the 1930s. There was one curious anomaly: the front-wheel-drive Citroen *Onze Legère* was included, though it was vintage in neither conception or appearance. It just happened, though, that many VSCC members were running FWD Citroens as everyday transport. . . .

Until 1951, the VSCC was primarily concerned with—as its title proclaimed—vintage *sports* cars; less fiery machines were catered for that year by the formation of a Light Car Section within the VSCC, which encompassed non-sporting vintage cars developing less than 30 bhp, such as Morris, Clyno, and Jowetts. Some of the more diehard members looked down on such humble machinery with scorn, but they were all vintage.

Not so, however, their counterparts of the 1930s, a good proportion of which was, of course, still in everyday use by the undiscerning public. Once these owners had ditched their 1930s vehicles, and they had passed into the hands of enthusiasts, there began a groundswell of opinion calling for some recognised classification for such vehicles which, if they were not so quaint as their vintage predecessors, at least represented an important stage in motoring history. But these workaday 1930–40 vehicles remain without a distinctive title: 'Georgian' was suggested in the mid-1960s, but was not taken up for obvious reasons.

Some newer vehicles are occasionally referred to as 'special interest', but so far this term has not coalesced sufficiently to become of much use to the historian: the author has recently seen an Austin A35 of the mid-1950s, which breed was never special nor interesting, so defined. . . .

But there are more definitions worth considering: 'antique' and 'classic'. Emanating from the far side of the Atlantic, these admittedly portmanteau terms have more subdivisions within them than a Biblical family tree. Basically 'Antique' equals pre-1925, and 'Classic' is applied to distinctive motorcars produced between 1925–1942.

The reason for the earlier cut-off date in America is that there the mass-production era came earlier, and the typical American car of the late 1920s was a pretty drab animal. One could argue that on similar grounds, the British vintage classification ought to end with 1927: but fortunately nowadays, the old guidelines are used wisely.   DBW

SHAKE, RATTLE AND ROLL

Vibration in cars can literally shake them to pieces

VIBRATIONS IN A MOTOR CAR absorb energy and they can cause noise and discomfort. Bodywork vibrations usually generate noise only between 20 and 15,000 cycles per second. (Frequencies higher than this, though inaudible, can still be tiring.) The vibrations, usually occurring as road noise, are best eliminated by good design; suspension components should be mounted on rubber and the body, if it is separate from the chassis, should be on rubber mountings. Body panel vibration can be managed by stick-on pads.

More serious vibrations are often encountered through the steering wheel, usually indicating that a wheel is out of balance. Certain steering and suspension systems are more susceptible than others to this defect. Mcpherson strut suspension and worm and peg steering on some cars has made them notoriously sensitive to unbalanced wheels.

Wheels that are out of balance must be checked for both static and dynamic balance. A static balance is indicated when one part of the wheel is heavier than the rest; the wheel will tend to rotate until the heavy part rests at the bottom, and the wheel will seem to hop. A dynamic imbalance will cause heavy parts to exist on opposite sides of the wheel so that when it rotates it will tend to wobble. Each type of imbalance can be corrected by adding lead weights to the wheel rim.

Occasionally, an eccentric tyre may be found. This will cause a vibration that may not be detectable on a wheel-balancing machine. To detect such vibration, a piece of chalk should be held, steadily and lightly, against the tread and the wheel rotated. High and low points on the tyre will then be obvious.

A vibration that can be felt throughout the car but which does not affect the steering may be caused by an out-of-balance rear wheel; or by a worn universal joint on the propeller shaft. Propeller shafts are usually balanced before they are fitted and unless they are bent, will not normally cause vibration. If, however, one of the universal joints becomes worn, the shaft will be thrown to one side as it rotates. The only remedy is the fitting of a new universal joint.

Engine vibrations are transmitted by air (usually as noise), by the engine mountings to the vehicle, and the connections to the engine, such as the gear change and throttle linkages. Transmission of vibrations via these media can be considerably reduced by careful design, or even by simple modifications. Accoustic insulation in the engine compartment is the first step, in the form of heavy felt or thick plastic foam.

It is useful, too, to insulate mechanical linkages with the engine by rubber components wherever possible. With gaiters and rubber knobs fitted to gear levers, body panels subdued with anti-drumming pads, and additional felt on the floor, car noise becomes more tolerable.

Engine vibrations are complex, being caused by the numerous moving parts inside an internal combustion engine. Reciprocating pistons are balanced by transmitting forces to the crankshaft and counterbalanced by a rotating weight. Pistons are the major contributors to engine vibration; but the valve gear assembly and all rotating parts, such as the flywheel, water pump, generator and oil pump, none of which can be so perfectly balanced as to eliminate all vibration, also contribute to general engine stresses and vibrations.

Certain engines are more vibration prone than others. For example: a large single-cylinder engine will produce greater vibration than an engine of the same capacity with several cylinders. The pulsating gas pressures in a single-cylinder engine are greater and more infrequent than in a multi-cylinder engine, and are therefore more difficult to absorb.

Twin-cylinder engines, although easier to silence in the exhaust and inlet, are still very vibration-prone. British motor-cycle manufacturers have, traditionally, built two-cylinder engines in which the pistons reciprocate together. Many Japanese two-cylinder engines, in contrast, utilize a $180°$ crankshaft, and the pistons reciprocate alternately, considerably reducing vibrations. This does, however, cause the engine to run unevenly.

Four-cylinder V-formation engines are notoriously difficult to balance. Those in present-day production absorb a considerable amount of energy because of this very problem. It is not until the designer is in a position to utilize at least a straight four-cylinder engine that vibration becomes more manageable. NPG

Below: a Ford Granada and a Renault 16 on 'shake-down' tests. The Granada is on a rig which electronically simulates actual road surfaces. In one hour, the car can cover the equivalent of 36,000 miles of bumps and undulations

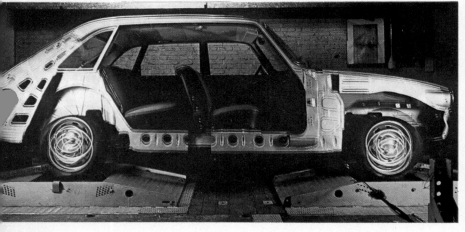

AN ITALIAN STYLING FAMILY

Like Pininfarina before them, the Vignale brothers started up their own styling house

ALFREDO VIGNALE was born in Turin on 15 June, 1913, the fourth of seven children, and after leaving school at the age of eleven began work as a helper in a local sheet-metal shop. The lad was a 'natural' panel-beater, completely drawn to the developing car industry. Indeed the whole Vignale family was involved with car bodywork, with his father and his brothers, Eusebio and Guglielmo, already employed as car painters.

Young Alfredo was a sufficient craftsman, however, to gain employment with Pininfarina at the tender age of seventeen, working in the Corso Trapani. It was in fact a 'copycat' move—Farina himself had left school at eleven to work in his brother's carriage repair business, and had subsequently been trained by

mates attracted by the idea of independence from the big Pininfarina concern. Historically this proved to be the right time for firms like Vignale to launch themselves, for while the rest of Europe set about restoring its personal transportation system with fairly plebian cars, Italy blossomed. The Italians, more motoring-mad than ever and reacting with typical Latin excitement to the end of wartime grey-ness and shortage, were ripe to express themselves on the roads. And the vast Fiat organisation; just in the process of mobilizing Italy again, provided the means (Alfa Romeo and Lancia production was minute by comparison).

The Italian *carozzeria* had several things on their minds. The last big motor-racing event before the

Left: quite a few of Vignale's designs were on Maserati chassis. This is a Spyder based on the 3500

one of the established masters of coachbuilding, Alessio of Turin.

And just as a Farina family firm, Stabilimenti Farina, developed out of the involvement of brothers in car-making, so the Vignale family came together in 1939 when the brothers established a small workshop in Turin's Gruliasco district. They were ambitious to add their name to the growing list of Italian coach-building firms, of which firms were still relatively unknown outside their own country for several reasons; not the least of which was lack of an Italian middle-class to provide a big automotive market and also French domination of European styling. Still, these firms were well respected in car-conscious Italy.

The war delayed Vignale plans, but in 1946 a small workshop was again equipped and staffed by a handful of craftsmen, many of them Alfredo's former work-

lights went out over Europe had been the 1940 Circuit of Brescia, dominated by lightweight 328 BMWs in open and closed coupé form—a bit slab-sided, but well proportioned and of clean outline, and built for the German firm by Superleggera Touring of Italy. The thinking behind these cars had considerable effect on the Italian designers.

They also had Detroit designs of the early forties before them with their strong (if brash) styling of grilles and bonnets and great moulding possibilities of new plastic materials.

Logical progress based on these influences, together with Italy's apparent willingness to put car styling high on the list of priorities, and also a renewed appetite around the world for exoticism, classicism and a whiff of the blue Mediterranean, assured Italian designers of a market. And they had something else in their favour too—the worldwide fascination of the Mille Miglia, that breeding ground for high-speed aerodynamic sports cars and superb shop window for the best of Italian design.

The first post-war Mille Miglia, in 1947, saw the only pre-war car, a 1938 2.9 litre Alfa-Romeo coupé, harried by Fiats and Fiat-based Cisitalias, and although the Alfa won, the little specialist-bodied coupés and roadsters from Italy had made their mark internationally. It was in this atmosphere of excitement that Vignale prepared to launch his name. Now partnered by fellow-craftsman Angelo Balma, he had established a small workshop in the Via Cigliano, Turin, and had undertaken many types of light engineering fabrication outside the car field in order to get the business going.

But car body building was his aim, and like many other aspiring coachbuilders in the area, he took the Fiat 500 as a basis.

His first effort on a 500 was sufficiently interesting to attract international attention. He moved to bigger cars, and in 1948 he took a major styling prize with a drophead design on a Fiat 1500—the Grand Prix d'Europe at Juan les Pins. Carrozzeria Vignale had

joined the ranks of Italy's recognised car body designers. A number of styling exercises and short runs followed on Fiat, Lancia and Ferrari chassis.

Among Vignale's employees now was the young Giovanni Michelotti. His early work for his employer included some definite work on radiator grille design, firstly on the 1949 V16 BRM grand prix car, and then for Ferrari with the 340 America Spyder. The elliptical orifice with cubed grille placed well back set the pattern for sports and sports-racing car frontal treatment through the 1950s.

It was work on Ferrari chassis that enabled Vignale to rise to substantial international fame at this time. From 1950 to 1953 his works produced bodies for Ferraris won three Mille Miglias and one Carrera Panamericana. This was the dawning of sports-car racing's golden era, and enormous public attention focussed on the results of important races. It was therefore highly desirable for the coach-builder to see the car he had styled score over those bearing rival firms' designs—for the style houses of Italy the Mille Miglia was not a contest between marques so much as a trial of which Ferrari (since Ferrari dominated the entry lists during this period) would provide the ultimate publicity for which body-builder.

There was joy at Carrozzeria Vignale for instance, when their Berlinetta was driven to fifth place by Simon and Vincent in the 1952 Le Mans race proved

to be the sole survivor of the four 4.1 litre Berrari runners. But it was certainly surpassed by the celebration after the 1953 Mille Miglia, when three works Ferraris with Superleggera Touring bodies all retired and privately-entered Vignale-bodied Ferraris came first (Marzotto) and fourth (Cole).

Italian designers—like other national groups of stylists—readily borrowed and adapted each others' ideas at this time. An outstanding Vignale body for Ferrari's first 2.9 litre V12, the Type 250 Mille Miglia, was, for instance, unashamedly pinched by Alfredo's old employer, Pininfarina, the sole distinguishing difference being a squaring of the top windscreen corners. As a result of this cross-pollination, and in many cases downright plagiarism, the individual merits of the Italian styling houses were not widely apparent abroad, and for the public at large 'Italian styling' was a sufficient accolade in itself.

As the taste for Italian styling swept Europe, some exponents of it were fortunate enough to link themselves with big manufacturers (Farina's shaping of the BMC range is the most familiar example known to British motorists), but others found that the fame brought by motor sport publicity produced mainly orders for one-offs. Vignale, for example, never got into the mass-production big time.

But individual styling and coach-building for the cognoscenti did have its own rewards, and one project

Above left: the 1951 Ferrari 212 Export, which featured a 2560 cc engine

Above: Vignale's 250 Mille Miglia Ferrari Spyder

with others, he experiments both with fantasy and technique, and his cars first surprise and then convince you.' But as we have suggested, individuality in those days was very much in the eye of the Italian beholder. . . .

While Pininfarina dominated the 1950s with work for volume car makers, the smaller styling houses did have some outlets in popular cars. Boano was responsible for the Renault Dauphine, while Ghia did the Floride coupe and also the Kharmann-Ghia coupe for VW. Bertone worked for NSU. In Britain, Michelotti in due course established a reputation through the Triumph Herald and subsequently through other work for Standard-Triumph. Vignale carried out some consultancy work on the Standard Vanguard Series 3.

Vignale was however still a panel-beater at heart, and was therefore as interested in body-building as in styling. In 1961 he abandoned the small workshop in the Via Cigliano and moved to a 12,000 square meter factory behind the Fiat Mirafiore factory still in the Grugliasco district. Alfredo's brother Guiseppi was in charge of administration, his old partner Balma left the firm, and Balma's son Giovanni was appointed sales manager. Bigger though the firm was

Below: a view of Vignale's '68 Matra, with its pop-up headlights retracted

Below left: A Maserati Sebring Spyder of 1965

Bottom: the Vignale De Tomaso City Car of 1970

often led to another. Vignale's special Ferrari for Princess Liliana de Rethy, for instance, led to work on an Aston Martin chassis for a Belgian customer, Baldovino, and that in turn provoked a wealthy New Jersey businessman to send him a Rolls-Royce chassis for special clothing. These toothsome individual cars, and his styling exercises on smaller cars at motor shows, earned for Vignale the description in the influential Italian publication 'Tuttosport' in April 1954 as 'the most personal and independent artist we know—his style has nothing in common

becoming, it was still very much 'in the family', and Vignale's interest and involvement was wholly personal and close.

Production of special bodywork on Fiat floorpans and running gear was now the main operation, firstly on the 600, then on the 850, with saloon, coupe and spyder versions. While these provided the bread and butter, Vignale—like other styling houses—produced numerous experimental studies for car makers and also the now almost obligatory display of motor show prototypes to proclaim to the world, and hopefully to the car-manufacturing customers, how provocative a stylist Alfredo Vignale was.

These were based on a variety of chassis. In 1963 his work embraced the Fiat 1000, Lancia Flavia and Sebring Maserati 3500 GTi. The following year he did a spyder version of the Maser, a Fiat 850, and a Compagno body on a Daihatsu. 1965 saw a coupe sportivo Fiat 850, and coupe and spyder versions of the Opel Kadett.

This year saw Vignale's first contact with the firm which was to give him one of his strongest connections with the British market. The management at Jensen was split over the replacement model for their C-V8, but it was eventually agreed that the new car should be styled and built in Italy. Design and development manager Kevin Beattie visited Ghia, Superleggera Touring and Vignale, and asked each to submit designs for the new car.

Ghia were heavily involved with Chrysler at this time, and demanded a fee to divert their efforts to Jensen. Vignale produced a rather conventional-looking design—similar to that for the four-door Maserati Mexico which he had introduced at the 1965 Turin motor show, and Jensen were looking for a more dramatic treatment. This came from Touring, and Jensen liked it, but the Milan firm was in such a financial pickle that Jensen had no confidence in its ability to produce the car.

Jensen bought the design outright, removed Touring's marks from the drawings, put Jensen's name on them, and took them along to Vignale as representing the sort of thing they had in mind. Even if Alfredo Vignale knew or guessed that Touring was the originator he said nothing, being anxious to secure the order for final styling and building.

With the deal signed and the tooling arranged it took Vignale only four months to produce a prototype car combining the proven C-V8 chassis and running gear and the new body. Within a further six months the first Italian-bodied, American-engined, British-built Jensen Interceptor was assembled at West Bromwich—one of the fastest international model operations on record.

Vignale's part in it did not last long, however. By October 1966, when two or three trimmed and painted Interceptor bodies were already arriving from Turin each week, Jensen had already decided that the finish was not what they wanted, and that the Vignale arrangement was financially unsound and too long-range for comfort and logic. Vignale was bought off, and the jigs and press tools transferred to Britain.

Jensen later admitted, however, that it took their own craftsmen a long time to match the flexibility and quality of work of the Italians.

Vignale meanwhile maintained his styling name with design studies. Notwithstanding the untimely loss of the Jensen manufacturing contract he showed a very elegant Interceptor-based two-seater coupe design, the Nova, at the 1967 Geneva motor show. Then he returned to Maserati with an Indianapolis body at the 1968 Turin show and with his namesake, the 4200

Vignale coupé, the following year.

He continued too to build on Fiat floorpans and mechanicals, and in 1967 his main models were marketed in Britain by a West London gaming company, F. Demetriou Group, of Queensway, W2. This curious arrangement arose after Greek-Cypriot casino owner Frixos Demetriou became concerned about the security of his gaming licence in Britain.

Seeking a watertight status as a 'legitimate businessman' in case his claim to operate his casino in Britain was challenged under a forthcoming review of the gaming laws, he decided to import cars, and signed an agreement with Vignale to become the sole UK concessionaire for Vignale models. A large car showroom next to Demetriou's Olympic Casino was bought, and a business partner, German-Swiss Ernest Huppert, ran the operation.

Four Vignale-Fiat models were marketed—the amusing and diminutive GaOine, based on the Fiat 500 floorpan and running gear but with drophead 'Noddy-car' body: the 850 Special Coupe based on the standard Fiat 850 S but with two-plus-two body and full specification: the Eveline Coupe SL, a two-door four-seater using the Fiat 124 and again offering a full specification: and the Samantha, another two-door

Right: Vignale's version of the mid-engined Matra 530 seen in 1968. This design was much cleaner and sleeker than the original

Below: the Vignale-bodied Maserati 3500 GT

Below right: on this Vignale design one wonders how much a replacement windscreen would cost

coupe, based on the Fiat 125 with luxurious specification and a five-speed gearbox option.

All these cars had Turin-built steel bodies and combined reasonable accommodation with styling that was considerably more fetching than the three-box Fiat original bodies. Demetriou arranged through Turin that Fiat (GB) should distribute and service the Vignale-Fiat cars—much to the annoyance of Fiat (GB) executives who were not a party to the agreement, who were suspicious of Vignale's work and its effect on warranty, and who feared that the cars would divert up-market Fiat customers away from the factory product. The Olympic Casino, where the import office was located, rang with many a multilingual argument over this, by all accounts.

Importation continued for two years. Several hundred cars were sold, and considerable ambitions were harboured for the future, including participation in saloon car racing, to which end a transporter was bought and racing driver Nick Faure was tentatively engaged for the season.

But in 1970 Demetriou's British gaming licence was renewed and he also secured new gaming outlets in Greece. His interest in the Vignale-Fiat project suddenly evaporated. Although the project had cost him an estimated £350,000, Demetrious was a

wealthy man and had no hestitation in dropping the car business and going to Greece.

He died there shortly afterwards crushed to death in the wreckage of a parked Vignale-Fiat which was run over by an army tank.

In Turin meanwhile, insufficient work brought hard times at the Vignale factory, and when in 1969 Alessandro de Tomaso, president of Ghia, was shopping for factory space to build his Pantera cars to be marketed by the Ford Motor Company, he found a sad but resigned vendor in Alfredo Vignale. On 16 November 1969, the very day that he signed the agreement to sellout, Vignale died in a car crash near the factory. He was 56.

The factory then went into Pantera production, making 16 bodies a day and sending them to de Tomaso at Modena for the assembly operation. In 1972 it seemed that the final trace of the Vignale origins was to go, for the factory became known as De Tomaso Automobili of Grugliasco. Respite came in 1973 when Ghia was purchased by Ford and the whole De Tomaso operation was re-named Vignale. The Modena plant was closed at the same time, even a sit-in by 150 workers failed to secure its continued operation.

Pantera production was then carried out for a period at the old Vignale Grugliasco factory—now of 40,000 square meters—but Pantera became a casualty of the world recession of 1974 and the factory closed down at the end of the year with the loss of 200 jobs.   EF

The world champion teacher

LUIGI VILLORESI was born in Milan on 16 May 1909, and began racing in 1931 at the same time as his elder brother Emilio. In the 1935 Coppa Ciano *voiturette* event at Montenero his modified Fiat sports car was third, and the following year he was third again in the same event driving a Maserati. He showed his versatility in 1936 as a class winner in the Monte Carlo Rally.

In 1937, driving a Maserati 6CM (he remained faithful to the Maserati *marque* for many years), Villoresi won the *voiturette* event at Masaryk, his first major victory. The following year saw him winning the Albi Grand Prix, the Pescara *voiturette* race and the Circuit of Lucca. In a works 3-litre Grand Prix Maserati 8CTF he was second at Naples and made fastest lap in the Coppa Acerbo at Pescara. The 1939 season was bitter: his brother Emilio was killed in an Alfa Romeo 158 at Monza. Nevertheless, Luigi decided to carry on his racing activities and his tally for the year was highlighted with victory in the South African Grand Prix, the Circuit of Abazzia and the Targa Florio.

Villoresi was quick to resume motor racing in 1946, now white-haired after a long period as a prisoner of war. He was one of the most accomplished drivers of the immediate post-war era, taking his works Maserati 4CL to victory in the Nice Grand Prix and Circuit of Voghera and placing second at Modena. He participated in the

The spoils of victory were part and parcel of Luigi Villoresi's motor-racing life

Indianapolis 500-mile race in a 3-litre Maserati 8CL, being the only European entry to qualify, and finished seventh. Together with Jean-Pierre Wimille of France, Villoresi was considered the best European racing driver. He was Italian Champion in 1947 and 1948.

In 1947 Villoresi's Maserati 4CL took him to victory at Lausanne, Nice, Strasbourg and Nimes and the Buenos Aires and Mar del Plata Grands Prix in Argentina. His South American success was repeated the following year when he won the two Buenos Aires Grands Prix; he also won the first post-war British Grand Prix at Silverstone, at Comminges, Albi and Penya Rhin and was second in the Italian Grand Prix and at San Remo with his 1½-litre Maserati 4CLT/48. Driving an 1100 cc OSCA he won the Naples Grand Prix. Now 39, in 1949 Villoresi and his 'pupil' Alberto Ascari, the 30-year-old son of famous pre-war exponent Antonio Ascari, joined the new Ferrari team. Villoresi had tremendous success with both Formula One and Formula Two models from the stable of the Prancing Horse, winning at Rome, Luxembourg, Brussels, Garda and Zandvoort. He was second in the Belgian and Swiss Grand Prix and third in the *Daily Express* Trophy at Silverstone. Earlier in

the year he had finished second twice in Argentina and won the Interlagos Grand Prix in Brazil.

In 1950 Villoresi won the Buenos Aires, Rosario, Marseilles and Monza Autodrome Grands Prix plus the Circuit of Erlen; he was also second at Rome, San Remo, Mons, Zandvoort, Pau and Luxembourg. But then he had a serious accident at Geneva, crashing badly and being deposited in the middle of the track where fellow-Italian and arch-rival Giuseppe Farina had to crash to avoid him. There was talk that Villoresi would never race again, but his reply to the gossip was victory in the 1951 Mille Miglia driving a new 4.1-litre Ferrari 340 America. He also won the Marseilles, Syracuse and Pau Grands Prix, the Circuit of Genoa, Circuit of Senigalia and Coppa Inter-Europa at Monza.

A touring car accident caused him to miss several races in 1952, but he bounced back to win Formula One races at Turin and Boreham and was second in a *formula libre* event at Silverstone. In a Formula Two Ferrari 500 he won at Sables d'Olonne, was second at La Baule and third in the Dutch and Italian Grands Prix.

Now well over 40, Villoresi gave no signs of giving up race driving. He showed the old skill was still there by winning the 1953 Tour of Sicily and Monza sports car races, was second at Bordeaux, Casablanca and Buenos Aires and third in the Italian Grand Prix. In 1954 he was invited to join the new Lancia team alongside Alberto Ascari, but the new D50 Grand Prix car project was delayed until the very end of the year so from time to time Villoresi was 'borrowed' by Maserati. In the Italian Grand Prix at Monza he drove one of his best-ever races, urging his Maserati 250F into the lead only for it to blow-up shortly after half-distance. His season was punctuated by another serious accident during practice for the Mille Miglia; Villoresi overturned his Lancia while trying to avoid a private car on the route of the famous 1000-mile race. His family begged him to retire. He refused.

In 1955 Villoresi remained with the Lancia Formula One team, finishing third at Turin and Syracuse before the team pulled out of racing early in the year following Ascari's fatal accident. But still Villoresi carried on, driving a Formula One Maserati for Scuderia Centro-Sud plus an OSCA sports car. It was with one of the latter machines that he crashed badly in the October 1956 Rome Grand Prix, suffering multiple fractures of his right leg. Early in 1957 he reluctantly announced his retirement from racing after a 25-year career which included over 50 major victories. He was not *quite* finished, however. In 1958, at the age of 48, he drove a Lancia in the Acropolis Rally—and won.   MK

THE CARS THAT RAN 'SILENTLY'

The Vinot-Deguingand company proudly called their cars La Silencieuse when they marketed them in England

FIRST ANNOUNCED IN 1901, this marque was originally built in Puteaux, near Paris, later in Nanterre; The early models were marketed in England under the name 'La Silencieuse', and were fairly advanced machines for the day, with vertical twin 5½ hp engines mounted in a pressed steel chassis with belt and chain final drive.

As the cars got bigger (in 1903 there were a 10 hp twin and 14 hp and 18 hp fours) they took the retrograde step of adopting armoured wood chassis. However in 1905 the larger cars in the range were back with pressed steel chassis, and a comprehensive line-up of models was offered. At the 1906 Crystal Palace Automobile Show, the English agents, T. J. Harman & Company of Regent Street, offered

12/16 hp of 2212 cc, a 14/20 hp of 2799 cc, a 20/30 hp of 3666 cc, a 30/45 hp of 5817 cc and a 35/50 hp 6-cylinder of 6999 cc. Prices ranged from £320 to £930.

The cars were represented at Olympia at the end of that year, but by the end of the following season the English agency had changed hands and was now operated by the coachbuilders William Cole & Sons of Kensington. Their 1907 Olympia stand featured the new 16/24 hp model with shaft-drive and four-speed gearbox, which was priced at £440 in chassis form. They also exhibited a landaulette limousine on this chassis, costing £700 complete and seating seven. An electric light was fitted to the interior of the body. On the 24/32 hp chassis, which was new

Above: a Vinot at Deguingand on the 1905 Rally du Compiègne

2491

Above: a superb example
of a 1910 Vinot

Right: a Vinot 15.9 hp
circa 1912

Below right: a 1914
12 hp

L-head and improved lubrication.

There was a total revision of the range in 1911, which saw a new 10/12 hp of 1693 cc with a monobloc engine, which cost £280 with two-seated torpedo bodywork, a 15.9 hp of 2212 cc, priced at £425 with four-seated touring bodywork and a 25/30 hp of 4166 cc which, fitted with all-weather four-seated coachwork, cost £650.

The year 1912 saw the marque's first serious entry into competition, with a team of three specially-built cars competing in the Coupe de l'Auto. These had F-head ioe engines and well-streamlined bodywork with long tails. Drivers were the brothers Léon and Lucien Molon and Vonatum; the latter achieved the marque's best placing in this event by coming in seventh. The Molons also took part with these cars in the Grand Prix de France and finished third and fifth.

There was little change in the touring models of Vinot before the Great War, apart from the introduction of a new 15/20 hp model of 2614 cc in 1913, the same year that an increase in stroke brought the swept volume of the 25/30 hp up to 4807 cc.

The Vinot stand at the 1919 Olympia Motor Show was entirely occupied by 15/20s little changed from their pre-war counterparts except for an inflated price and the adoption of electric lighting and starting. Most British Vinot models at that time seemed to be fitted with Park Ward coachwork.

Vinot's *alter ego*, Gladiator, expired in 1920, and the following year came the first new post-war model, the 1795 cc 11/25 hp, of conventional design save for the adoption of alloy pistons and overhead valves; the use of pump and splash lubrication was a definite step back compared with pre-war models. The 15/20 also acquired overhead valves in 1922, when it was designated Type BO.

Vinot sales were apparently falling off by this time as the company was trying to drum up orders with a guarantee that should chassis prices be reduced before 30 June 1921, the difference in purchase price would be refunded to the customer.

The 11/25 was a typical French light car, with a V radiator similar in appearance to that of the DFP; the British Vinot company obviously wished to upgrade the car's social standing with advertising that waxed lyrical; 'Now that the better weather is with us once again, your thoughts undoubtedly have turned to the beauties and health-giving properties of the countryside, in short, where you feel the 'joy of living.' Nothing will help you more to realise these pleasures than the 11/25 hp Vinot BP Model. It is built for that purpose.'

At the 1923 Olympia Show, a new 12/25 hp Vinot appeared; this was the 11/25 bored out to give a capacity of 1847 cc and now available with the option of front wheel brakes at an extra cost of £25 on the chassis price of £425.

Front wheel brakes were standard the following year, but there was a warning of impending disaster at Olympia, where the Vinot stand was shared by Donnet-Zedel. In fact, Donnet-Zedel had just acquired the Vinot factory at Nanterre, and no more Vinots were seen at Olympia, though the marque continued a shadowy existence for another couple of years. However, there was a new Deguingand light car with a 735 cc Duplex engine and sub-basic engineering in 1928, designed by Marcel Violet, who had previously conceived the Violet-Bogey cyclecar. But this last vestige of the old Vinot-Deguingand concern lost its identity in 1932 and was rechristened as a Donnet. It lasted only a year before Donnet itself was extinct and its factory acquired by Simca. DBW

that year, they exhibited a full limousine, again with seven seats and 'fitted with two chairs, three electric lights, canteen, cigar lighter, silk velvet curtains etc.' This model cost £860 complete.

A year later, the agency had reverted to Harmans, and all models shown at Olympia now had shaft drive. Vinot acquired Gladiator in 1909, and the two marques differed only in the design of their radiators for the next decade; with the initial difference that the 24 hp model was only available as a Vinot.

By 1910, Vinot were controlling their own destinies in England, with an office in Great Portland Street, London. A new 12/16 hp model appeared with a monobloc engine and pressure lubricated crankshaft, while the 25/30 hp was demonstrated and had an

SPECTACULAR AND EFFICIENT CARS FROM FRANCE

Gabriel Voisin claimed to be the builder of the first practical aeroplane; but he definitely did build spectacular V12 motor cars

GABRIEL-EUGÈNE VOISIN, born on 5 February 1880, was one of the most remarkable figures in the history of transportation in France. Having made his fame in one element, the air, after World War I he turned to car manufacture, producing some of the most original —and potent—vehicles of the 1920s, cars designed for function and efficiency which eschewed all the conventional tricks of the stylist.

It was almost inevitable that Voisin should become an engineer—his father Georges Voisin, was a graduate of the Paris Arts et Metiers school who had become a metal founder, and was himself the son of an engineer. But Georges was an irresponsible character, unlucky in business and a wine-bibber, who committed suicide when the boy was six, and Gabriel and his brother Charles were brought up by their mother in the household of her father, who worked as an engineer in a gas works.

Among their numerous escapades, the boys acquired considerable skill in converting scrap metal into such artefacts as boats and shotguns; Gabriel's skill was augmented by a course at the Beaux-Arts school at Lyon, where he learned all aspects of engineering drawing, to which he added a natural talent for visualising mechanical components 'in the round'.

Around 1898 the brothers experimented with gliders, then, with the winnings from a lucky coup at the gaming tables in Nice, Gabriel bought a vehicle known as an Automoto tricycle, whose mechanical components proved to lack the stamina necessary for touring, taking six days to cover the 310 miles from Nice to Neuville. But the Automoto inspired Voisin to draw up plans for a proper car, which, thanks to a legacy, he was able to construct in 1899, using a second-hand chassis, which he adapted to make an underslung type and a 5 hp single-cylinder Aster engine. It proved reliable until Gabriel ran over a pig; then, thanks to the vehicle's low build, there was a considerable derangement of the car's internal economy. . . .

After this, Voisin devoted himself to his studies of architecture—and to the amorous adventures which were an essential part of his life—then, in 1900, Gabriel and Charles once again began experimenting with gliders. In 1904 Ernest Archdeacon, a wealthy friend of Gabriel's, put up the money to form a 'Syndicat d'Aviation', of which Gabriel Voisin was 'engineer', at a salary of Fr190 a month. By 1907, Voisin had built a powered heavier-than-air machine which had made observed flights, in 1908 a circular kilometre course was flown under full control and in 1910 the Avions Voisin factory was built by Gabriel and a few friends in the Avenue Gambetta, opposite the Issy-les-Moulineaux *champ de manoeuvres* on the outskirts of Paris.

From that point in time until the end of the Great War, it was Voisin's success as an aircraft constructor that dominated his life, and during that period the

Issy factory turned out some 10,000 aircraft—or as Voisin had it, '*cerfs-volants*' ('kites'). But the Armistice meant that there was no demand for warplanes— nor was there much immediate future in civil aviation. An attempt to build prefabricated houses was opposed by the entire French building industry.

So he decided to return to his old love, the motor car. After a mercifully brief flirtation with powered attachments for bicycles and with cyclecars, Voisin acquited the rights to a design which Andre Citroen had been considering for mass-production before he decided to concentrate on the 1.3 litre Type A. The model which he made over to Voisin was hardly suited to mass-production in the Ford idiom, anyway, for it was a 4-litre car with a Knight sleeve-valve engine: it had originally been developed by two employees of Panhard named Artaud and Dufrène,

Below: a 1923 Voisin C3 tourer; it was powered by a four-cylinder, sleeve-valve engine and, like all Voisins of that period, was immensely strong, extremely refined and very quiet

Top: the very stylish Voisin C11 Sport of 1927; it was fitted with Dewandre vacuum servo brakes, a feature of all Voisins from late 1925

Above left: a 1920 Voisin 25/35 hp four-door saloon. Note the impressive disc wheels

who had bought the prototype and the design from their employer and offered them to Citroen, who thought the concept too luxurious.

But Voisin took on Artaud ('a skilled odd-job man') and Dufrène ('a fully trained engineer') and their design, and abandoned aviation. In November 1918 he organised his production team: the victory celebrations were still going on when the first Voisin chassis was completed. It was ready for trials on the frozen surface of Issy aerodrome in February 1919, when Voisin discovered that the back axle had been assembled 'wrong way round', resulting in one speed forward and four in reverse. Not at all daunted, he tried the backward paces of the car and discovered that it pulled up far more steadily in *marche arrière* than when it was going in the normal direction. As the car had brakes only on the rear wheels, Voisin concluded that front-wheel-braking was obviously

more efficient, and from an early date Voisin cars had brakes on all four wheels.

Four 18CV Voisins were shown at the 1919 Paris Salon: these were a bare chassis, a skiff, a limousine and a saloon. Hallmark of the Voisin was a distinctive vee radiator, and liberal use was made of aluminium in the power unit to give a far more spirited performance than was usually associated with sleeve valves. Alloy pistons were standardised from the start, and lubrication was so arranged that the supply of oil to the sleeve valves was proportional to the speed of the engine.

The special merits of the Voisin design were amply demonstrated in the Touring Grand Prix of July 1922, in which Voisin cars came home one-two-three. The winner, veteran racing driver Rougier averaged 66.9 mph for 443.7 miles on a fuel allowance of 16.6 miles per gallon. Voisin's engineers had spent

Top: a 1932 Voisin tourer; note the unusual door panel finish and the stylish elegance of the car

Above: in 1927 Voisin produced this record breaker with a straight-eight engine of 8 litres; it set a world 24-hour record at an average speed of 113.4 mph

three months experimenting to achieve this result; Rougier finished with less than two gallons of petrol left in his tank.

Voisin's prewar motoring experiences had left him with a healthy respect for steam power, and indeed in 1920 he fitted a steam engine into an 18CV chassis for experimental purposes. He came to the conclusion that what was needed was an internal combustion engine with the flexibility and silence of steam, which resulted in the construction of a sleeve-valve V-12 luxury car, which appeared at the 1921 Paris Salon; in prototype form it had only two forward speeds, but development troubles meant that the design never reached production status.

Instead, from 1921, there was a new, small, but still luxurious, Voisin, the 1244 cc 8CV. With this model, Gabriel Voisin's flair for designing coachwork which put practicality before elegance began to assert itself; the early Voisins had been as elegant as you please, and had attracted the custom of celebrities as diverse as the President of France and Josephine Baker, as Rudolph Valentino and H. G. Wells. But some 8CVs had tartan fabric coachwork and uncompromisingly squarecut appearance. An enlarged version, the 1551 cc 10CV, appeared in 1925; in 1926 this was available with production line four-seat, two-door coachwork scaling less than 5 cwt; 'The body lines,' commented W. F. Bradley dryly, 'are distinctively French, having a sobriety which might not at first appeal to English tastes.' Built up in sections on jigs, the new coachwork was based on a wood and sheat aluminium tray bolted to the chassis, and stiffened by metal ribbing; footwells for the passengers' feet kept the centre of gravity low. Both the 18CV and the 10CV remained in production throughout the 1920s; they were joined in 1927 by light sixes based on Voisin's Grand Prix racing experience. The touring development of this model was the 13CV of 2.3 litres; this was the most successful

of the Voisin models, achieving sales of some 8000 (or around a third of total production) in a decade. There was a 4.5 litre six in 1927, which gradually supplanted the old 18CV.

In 1929 Voisin built two V-12s, one of 3.9 litres, the other of 4.9 litres, but V-12 output was always low. There were experiments, too, with the De Lavaud semi-automatic transmission, which almost reached production . . . but was superseded by a Cotal preselector gearbox.

The Voisins of the 1930s, which included the legendary straight-12, whose engine penetrated the driving compartment in the interests of perfect weight distribution, were cloaked in coachwork whose bizarre appearance has perhaps been softened by the passage of time, but which were the subject of much controversy in their day, even in France (which was the home of eccentric bodywork at that period and which has always had more sympathy for the *jolies laides* than any other nation).

Voisin lost control of his company in 1937, and the new incumbents produced a horrid confection with a supercharged Graham engine, the first Voisin car with a poppet-valve engine. Gabriel Voisin took over again in 1939, but the day of the Voisin car was over, and Issy was turned over to the manufacture of aeroengines. Total output of Voisin cars amounted to some 27,000.

During the war, Voisin experimented with steam power again; after the hostilities he developed a modern cyclecar, the 125 cc Biscuter, which was produced under licence in Spain, where a more powerful 200 cc Hispano-Villiers engine was used.

Voisin died in 1973, aged 93; his restless mind was always looking forward. Typical of the man was the comment he made to an enthusiast who sought his advice on the restoration of a vintage Voisin—'you are too young to worry about old cars: at your age you should be concerned with women!' DBW

A CLASS APART FROM THE GRANDS PRIX

Voiturette racing was designed to cut the enormous costs of racing in the early part of the century. It was to become Formula Two

LEON BOLLÉE registered the name *voiturette* for his little sporting tricar of 1895; but the term was so easily memorable that it soon became used for any light car. However, the first voiturette class to appear in motor racing was true to the term's origins, for it was composed entirely of Bollées. It happened in the 1896 Paris–Marseilles contest, in which class C was for any vehicle which was not a motor car nor a motor cycle—and this meant Bollées.

In any case, cylinder capacities of even the largest cars of the period were still quite modest—the Panhards racing in Paris–Marseilles had engines of only 1396 cc. There was little point in basing a voiturette class on swept volume.

The 1897 Paris–Dieppe still had an all-Bollée voiturette class—and Jamin's Bollée shamed all the larger and theoretically more powerful vehicles by coming in first overall, averaging 25.2 mph for the 106.2 mile race.

For the 1898 season, however, the first genuine attempt to separate the large cars from the small was made, again in the Paris–Marseilles, in which the Bollées were now relegated to the motorcycle category, and cars were divided into two categories, one for cars weighing over 400 kg, and cars weighing between 200–400 kg, with side-by-side seating for two people: thus 'the light vehicles were protected from the abnormal racing car.' But there were only two entries in the class, a Georges Richard and a Parisienne, and their performance was so minimal that they could do no better than 21st and 23rd overall.

The generic term 'voiturette' was first applied in the 1899 Paris–St Malo race; the same year the first race

for this class of vehicle only was organised by *Sport Universal Illustré* from Paris to Rambouillet and back, and proved a triumph for Louis Renault.

Hitherto, the term 'voiturette' had been applied at the whim of race organisers: but at last in 1901 a firm classification was laid down. It remained in force for the next six years, and established a voiturette as a car weighing between 250–400 kg. From 400–650 kg came *voitures legéres*, while *grandes voitures* weighed over 650 kg (and less than 1000 kg from 1902).

It was first applied in the 1901 Paris–Bordeaux, in which the class was dominated by Renault cars of 8 hp, Louis Renault's class-winning car also coming twelfth in the overall results and proving faster than most of the nominally more powerful *voitures legéres*.

Renaults again headed the class result lists in the major race of 1901, Paris–Berlin. Louis Renault's class-winning average of 36.9 mph for the 687 miles on his 1021 cc single-cylinder Renault compared very favourably with the performance of the outright winner, Fournier, who averaged 44.1 mph on a Mors of 10,088 cc, and earned him eighth place overall, ahead of any of the *voitures legéres*.

Inevitably, as the manufacturers became more skilled at building lighter chassis, so the voiturettes, just like the larger cars, began to have larger and larger engines installed: in the Paris–Madrid of 1903, the winning Clement had an 18 hp four-cylinder engine of 2290 cc, and a competing Darracq was endowed with an even larger power unit, a 20 hp four of 3770 cc.

It was to eliminate such freakish machinery that the popular magazine *l'Auto* conceived a new voiturette

Below: the victorious Delage 3-litre car of the 1911 Coupe de l'Auto; the car had a power output of 50 bhp at 3000 rpm

Top: Georges Boillot poses in his 7½-litre Grand Prix Peugeot in 1912; Boillot was one of the more successful voiturette racers. This GP car is large, expensive and thirsty, quite unlike the smaller voiturette vehicles, and it was this reason that made the smaller class of racing popular

Above: built in the voiturette style was this 1902 De Dion Bouton

formula in 1905, in which engine capacity was to be limited to 1 litre, weight was to be restricted, and cars were to be subjected to a six days' trial before the event. Even though voiturette racing under the old regime had become almost non-existent, the new concept failed to reawaken interest in the class, and the 'Coupe de l'Auto', run off in November 1905, was a signal failure, with no overall winner—indeed, the results were annulled.

Undaunted, *l'Auto* exercised that famous French talent for compromise and totally recast the regulations for 1906, imposing a bore restriction to 120 mm for single-cylinder engines and 90 mm for twins—fours were not admitted—and stipulating a *minimum* car weight of 700 kg. This formula succeeded where its predecessor had failed, and interest in the new voiturette class was greatly stimulated, to the extent that for 1907 there were two front-line voiturette races—the Coupe de l'Auto and the Sicilian Cup. *L'Auto* once again altered the rules, reducing bore size to 100 mm for singles, 80 mm for twins, and setting a 670 kg weight limit for singles, 850 kg for twins. Both events were won by a marque exclusively associated with voiturettes, Sizaire-Naudin. M.

Naudin won both races (his partner, Sizaire, had won the 1905 Coupe de l'Auto), while De Dion Bouton and Lion-Peugoot were also strongly represented in the results.

There were four voiturette events in 1908, two in Italy (won by Guippone's Lion-Peugeot and two in France, the Grand Prix des Voiturettes, won by Guyot's Delage, and the Coupe de L'Auto (which now admitted four-cylinder cars, restricting their bore size to 65 mm, and again imposed maximum weight limits, of 500 kg for singles, 600 kg for twins and 650 kg for fours). Despite the changes, it was the 'old school' of voiturettes which dominated the results, with Naudin and Sizaire in the first two places, and Goux (Lion-Peugeot) third. As Grand Prix racing was now, by official decree, moribund, the Coupe de l'Auto took on new importance in the motor racing calendar, and became the training ground for some of the great racing drivers, such as Georges Boillot. Moreover, it promoted the development of high-efficiency engines of moderate displacement, and unwittingly helped to pave the way for a new generation of Grand Prix cars.

For 1909, there were yet more changes to the formula: all cars were limited to a weight of 600 kg, while single cylinder cars could have cylinder dimensions falling within the parameters 100 mm × 250 mm to 120 mm × 124 mm (1963 cc–1402 cc); twins could have dimensions between 80 mm × 192 mm (1930 cc) and 95 mm × 98 mm (1389 cc); fours were restricted to dimensions between 65 mm × 150 mm (1991 cc) and 75 mm × 75 mm (1325 cc). In theory the new regulations were intended to assist the development of light four-cylinder power units: in practice, they encouraged the building of freakish long-stroke single-cylinder power units, which dominated the results lists. Lion-Peugeots of *cathedralesque* appearance won all three main voiturette races of 1909, the Sicilian Cup and the Catalan Cup at Sitges falling to Goux, while his team mate Guippone took the Coupe de L'Auto itself. Fastest car in the Coupe race was Boillot's Lion-Peugeot, with cylinder proportions like a stove-pipe, and six valves—three inlet, three exhaust—crammed into its cylinder-head.

The high, narrow and ugly Lion-Peugeots continued to dominate the 1910 results, with Boillot, Guippone and Goux coming in one-two-three in

Above: another Delage voiturette victory. This is Guyot after winning the Grand Prix de Voiturettes at Dieppe in 1908

Right: this Hispano Suiza Sport of 1912 is another version of a car built in the voiturette mould

Sicily, and Goux and Boillot in the first two places at Sitges: but, significantly, multi-cylinder cars were now getting a look in, for third at Sitges was an Hispano-Suiza driven by Zuccarelli. Even longer strokes were permissible that year, and Lion-Peugeot responded by fielding V-4 racers with 65 mm × 260 mm engines (3451 cc) which proved highly unstable, with fatal results for Guippone. However, these freakish machines were soundly trounced by Zuccarelli's 65 mm × 200 mm Hispano (2655 cc), which finished first in the Coupe de l'Auto, followed by Goux's twin-cylinder Lion-Peugeot and Chasagne's Hispano. Boillot's V-4 Lion-Peugeot was fourth.

During 1911–13, the Coupe de l'Auto was once again the only front-line voiturette race, but now a maximum capacity of 3 litres was imposed, while bores and strokes had to fall within the ratios 1:1 to 2:1; in 1912, there was a minimum weight of 800 kg, in 1913 a maximum weight of 900 kg and a ban on forced induction.

Delage were victorious in 1911, while Sunbeam came one-two-three in the 1912 Coupe de l'Auto, which earned them fourth-fifth-sixth places in the Grand Prix, which was run concurrently with the Coupe to ensure a good entry. Thus voiturettes were

now able to defeat the racing monsters: and for 1914 Grand Prix cars had become virtual voiturettes, with a capacity limit of 4.5 litres.

The 1913 Coupe de l'Auto went to Peugeot, as did the Grand Prix: but voiturettes were now once again growing into full-size cars, and so 'Grand Prix' races for those most ephemeral of machines, the cyclecars, entered the racing calendar.

With the departure of the Coupe de l'Auto, the great days of voiturette racing were over. The series had proved a major catalyst in the development of the high-efficiency internal combustion engine, and subsequent events bearing the name voiturette were not nearly as significant.

As formula changes lowered the cylinder capacity of the Formula One racing cars of the day, so the need for a voiturette class diminished, though the term survived throughout the 1920s and 1930s—the ERA was just about the last car to bring any lustre to the term 'voiturette'.

But with all its freaks and failures, it was the Coupe de l'Auto which had really supplied the stimulus to the designers and manufacturers—without it, engine development could well have lagged in that doldrum period when the Grand Prix was in limbo.   DBW

PART OF RUSSIA'S TRANSPORTATION SYSTEM

The Volga company is part of Russia's state-controlled 'Soviet personal transportation pattern'

Right: a Volga four-door saloon in October 1961. One can see the obvious American late '50s influence on the styling

VOLGA is one of those Russian car names known to the West as a marque in its own right, but in fact the cars that carry the Volga badge are part of the wider Soviet personal transportation pattern, and need to be seen in the context of this pattern.

The story starts in 1946, in the aftermath of what the Russian's officially call the Great Patriotic War. Starved of transport, Russia needed a rugged, no-nonsense car quickly. A design team under Andrei Lipgart came up with a unitary-construction design with independent front suspension and semi-elliptic rear springs and rigid axle, powered by a 2.1 litre four-cylinder 50 bhp engine with three-speed synchromesh gearbox. It was called the Pobieda (meaning Victory), it emerged from the giant Gorky car plant, and was also known by the Russians as the GAZ M20. Further confusing the nomenclature was the title of the Gorky manufacturing operation, Zavod Imieni Molotova, whose initials form the much more familiar ZIM name.

Although a few changes were wrought on the Pobieda, including some touring versions and a four-wheel-drive M72 version in 1955, nothing dramatic happened to the model's appearance, and after thirteen years production the Russians decided that even

their severe weather and geographical conditions did not excuse the continued manufacture of the solid, stolid Pobieda. A new design, utilising Pobieda components but considerably up-dated in approach, was put into production alongside the old model. Over a three-year period the two assembly lines ran in parallel until, in 1958, conversion was complete. The Pobieda design was pensioned off for manufacture by FSO in Poland under the name of the Warszawa, and continued until quite recently when it was superseded by the Polski-Fiat. The new Gorky product meanwhile became known in the West as the Volga, a familiar name in export markets.

To the Russians it was the GAZ M21. Another Lipgart creation, it was one of the very first cars to use light alloys in mass-produced engines, and also pioneered the use of five main bearings in a four-cylinder engine. It displaced 2.5 litres, was of overhead-valve configuration, employed wet cylinder liners, and was offered with either a 70 or 97 bhp power plant under the bonnet.

Automatic transmission was introduced in 1959, but was not a success. Subsequent changes were confined mainly to grille design, and M22G estate and M22E ambulance versions were later added to the range. The Volga saloon, as the Pobieda before it, became one of Russia's most popular taxis. In Belgium the import firm, Sobimpex installed a 65 bhp Rover diesel as an option.

The next Volga development emerged in 1968 the GAZ M24 or Volga 24, with lower lines and longer wheelbase. Output was up to 110 bhp, with drive through a four-speed all-synchromesh gearbox with floor-mounted gearchange. The Volga 24 completely supplanted the older car by 1971, and became highly regarded within the Eastern bloc, winning gold medals at the Plovdiv and Brno international exhibitions, and taking a class win the Taurus-73 rally: none of which achievements were communicated to the West, but nor would they have meant much if even if they had been.

Latterly the Gorky factory has been extended to accommodate manufacture of a new V6 2.5 litre 160 bhp 7.5 to 1 sealed-unit engine, to be opened for overhaul only every 150,000 kilometers. This engine was designed by NAMI, the Moscow vehicle research centre for the modern Volga 24 and for a four-wheel derivative called the Volga Universal.

In 1973 a 24-02 estate car version of the Volga saloon was introduced with three rows of seats, and giving accommodation for a driver plus seven passengers or a driver, with the two rear seat in reclining positions, one passenger and 500 kg of cargo.

The Russian car industry has been fairly tidy about which factory has built which sort of vehicle. The Volga has become the nation's taxi. More splendid motoring fare has been provided by ZIS, ZIL and ZIM cars (each named after the factory that produced them). The medium market has been supplied by Moskvich, and latterly the Aporozhets and the Fiat 124-based Lada have opened up new light-car areas— and though the Russian home market is still in its infancy, at least the car industry has known exactly who was doing what, and wasteful internal competitive effort was avoided.

To eastern eyes the results of this well-regulated and competition-free industry show in the cars, but Russian designers have recently been demonstrating that they can learn how to meet worldwide standards of finish and performance, and with—at this time— possibly the world's healthiest motor industry, Russia is set to become a major force in many markets. The name of Volga, and other automotive products of the Soviet Union, could become rather better known in the West in the not too distant future.   EF

Below: the Volga type 24 that was built in the 1970s; it was powered by a four-cylinder engine of 110 bhp

Dr FERDINAND AND THE PEOPLE'S CAR

Ferdinand Porsche built the prototypes for the Beetle, the car which was to start Volkswagen off on many years of air-cooled success

FERDINAND PORSCHE, later Dr Ferdinand Porsche, was born in 1875 at the little village of Maffersdorf near Reichenberg (now Liberec) in the Austro-Hungarian Empire (now Czechoslovakia). In 1899 he joined Lohner & Co at Vienna as an electrical engineer and became, in 1906, technical Director at the Austro-Daimler factory at Weiner Neustadt. Ten years later he was managing director. He was a man who was very interested in small cars; a fact which resulted in 1922 in the creation of the famous Austro-Daimler built 'Sascha' racing cars with 1097 cc 4-Cylinder Double-OHC-engines. In 1923 Porsche left Austria and became chief-designer for Daimler at Untertürkheim near Stuttgart.

There he modified Paul Daimler-designed 2-litre 4-cylinder racing cars, created new 2-litre 8-cylinder racing cars and was also responsible for the famous supercharged 6.8 litre and 7.1 litre 6-cylinder Mercedes S, series. Afterwards in 1929 he returned to Austria and joined for a short period, the Steyr factory before founding a design office for the car industry at Stuttgart in 1930 under his own name.

Here, at this independent office the first sketches of a people's car were drawn and at about the same time, preliminary drawings for the sensational 16-cylinder 'Porsche' racer which eventually became the famous 'Auto Union' racer.

Porsche intended producing small cars at Austro-Daimler, but failed because of the opposition of other directors who could not see any commercial value in building small and cheap cars. He found an identical situation at Mercedes. Both factories produced middle-size and big cars. They had no intention nor means for the creation of new, big and ultra-modern factories for the manufacture of a big quantity small car.

It was 1931 when Porsche's design office at Stuttgart got an order from the Zündapp motorcycle factory to create a prototype of a small car of 1200 cc capacity with a 5-cylinder Radialengine. Three cars were made and tested, but Dr Fritz Neumayer, the then Zündapp boss, was not satisfied with the results and withdrew from the project. Soon afterwards another leading German motorcycle manufacturer, Fritz von Falkenhayn, the head of the NSU factory at Neckarsulm, approached Porsche with a view to building the small car. With an aircooled flat-four 1448 cc engine in the back, this car was much different from the original design made for Zündapp.

NSU sold their car factory at Heilbronn in 1930 to Fiat but intended to resume manufacture of the Porsche car at Neckarsulm. There they had an English designer, Walter-William Moore, in charge of motorcycle design. It was this man in 1933–34 who redesigned the Porsche flat-four engine.

At Neckarsulm five prototypes of the Moore-modified car were made. But at around the same time, 1934–35, motorcycle sales improved so much that NSU decided not to go on with the car. They returned

the prototypes to Porsche. And Porsche carried on in his design office, assisted by such capable men as Karl Rabe, Josef Kales and Franz X. Reimspiess.

Flat engines were not an invention of the thirties; Carl Benz built one as far back as 1898; many car and motorcycle factories used them soon afterwards. Porsche continued to create different prototypes with a view to production economies, but ran into many troubles in connection with power output, reliability and petrol consumption. Then, in 1934, came a demand from the Government of Germany via the 'Reichsverband der Automobil Industry' (Association of Car Manufacturers) for the design of a real People's Car. And a decision for the use of a flat four-cylinder ohv-engine.

Hitler's wish that Josef Ganz should create this car, could not be fulfilled. Ganz was not a 'clean' German, he was a Jew, who eventually had to leave Germany and went to Switzerland and eventually to

Above: two early versions of the legendary Beetle which was commissioned as the 'people's car'. Although over the years the car has been much modernised, the basic shape and the flat-four air-cooled engine remained. *Top,* is a 1939 example while, *above,* is a 1953 version

Australia. And so it was Porsche who built the prototypes with Governmental assistance . . . prototypes with 985 ccm flat aircooled four-cylinder ohv-engines in the rear. They had 70 mm bore, 64 mm stroke, 5.6 compression ratio and 23.5 bhp at 3000 rpm. A technical sensation, because it was a short-stroke power unit!

The first tests, conducted with three prototypes built to order by Porsche in 1936, took over two months and covered 150,000 km . . . with test drivers travelling between 750 km and 1500 km daily. During 1937 thirty further prototype VW's were running. As Porsches Design Office was not equipped for such

quantities, Daimler-Benz AG built these cars at the Untertürkheim Mercedes factory.

Adolf Hitler, the 'Führer', had already promised the Germans the ideal people-car. For 999 Reichsmark! And in May 1937 the 'Gesellschaft zur Vorbereitung des deutschen Volkswagens mbH' (Association for the preparation of the German People-Car) had been founded. A year later, on 26 May 1938, the first stone for the new factory was laid 80 km east of Hannover, at Fallersleben. And soon they called—officially—the new place which included more villages 'KdF-Stadt' (Strength through Joy-Town) because Hitlers KdF-Association stood behind the mammouth-project

Below: Beetles have not been too successful in competition. However, John Ivil here tries his best in a 'clubbie' rally in his 1963 car

Right: a 1973 variation on the Beetle platform, the 1600 Fastback

too. In September 1938 another foundation stone, this time for a new town for the workers, was laid. And the 'Volkswagenwerk GmbH' was created, mainly with money paid in advance for one of these cars. By the end of 1938, not less than 169,741 orders had arrived and been accepted.

There was now a full order book, a big factory, a big town 'in preparation' and . . . a war coming. Production commenced in 1940 with a modified version of the car, the 'bucket-car' made for military purposes. It was not until after 1945 that VW produced cars for the public, although the people who had already paid an advance in 1938 never got their cars. It was many years and many court-hearings before the problem of the pre-paid VW's was settled.

The bucket-car, had been equipped with a 1131 cc engine and 25 bhp. The original 985 cc power unit had not enough power for the cross-country going bucket-car. And when VW commenced production of 'normal' cars in 1945 it was considered that the original 985 cc unit was too small and the larger engine remained in production until 1954.

Two years after introducing the bucket-car, VW commenced production of the amphibian version. Seventy thousand of these 'Schwinmwagens' had been made during the war.

On 10 April 1945, the US Army arrived at Volkswagen's home, Wolfsburg; a town of seventeen thousand of whom nine thousand were VW employees. At that time 336,000 Germans had paid in advance 207,000,000 Reichsmark for VW cars. This amount was on a special account at the 'Bank für Deutsche Arbeit'. On 25 May 1945 the town known as 'KdF-Stadt' and as 'VW-Stadt' became officially Wolfsburg, and is now in the British Sector of the new Germany.

Production in 1945 was very limited; only 1785 cars—mainly for the British Army and the mail delivery services—left the factory, two thirds of which was in ruins. The major task in 1946 was to rebuild the works; yet more than 10,000 VW's were produced. The 1947 production figures dropped to 8,987 vehicles of which 56 went to the Netherlands, the first country to import VW cars.

Things went better in 1948, when Heinrich Nordhoff became General Manager of VW at Wolfsburg. By the end of May, 25,000 VW cars left the

modern assembly plant. Nineteen-forty-nine brought the first VW orders from America.

Until this point all VW cars were identical except for the colour. On 1 July the 'Export' version with improved equipment and the Kharmann-Ghia Cabriolet was shown for the first time. In February 1950 the TV-Transporter was added to the still very small VW range. In fact, the production of this Transporter was on a very limited scale with only ten units a day. Still, VW car production increased rapidly. Mainly because of the completion of the task of rebuilding the war damaged factories, but also because of the ever increasing demand for the reliable and comparatively cheap VW cars. Professor Nordhoff was the dynamic man behind the success.

Volkswagen Canada Ltd was created in 1953 and Volkswagen do Brasil SA followed a year later as sales and factory facilities respectively. In July 1953 the 500,000 VW left Wolfsburg. The situation was so good that Nordhoff declared a yearly bonus.

The Kharmann-Ghia coupé was the sensation of 1955 which also marked the first million VWs. Volkswagen of America was founded in 1955 to supply and service cars in America and the year ended with the average daily manufacture of cars up to one thousand.

In 1958 a new VW factory was opened at Kassel and engine production facilities were increased at the Hanover works. Transporter manufacture remained there. Another sales organisation 'Volkswagen France', was added in 1960 when the whole VW organisation was reshaped. As a result of it, 60 per cent of the VW shares have been sold to the public. The remaining 40 per cent remained with the county of Lower Saxonia (Niedersachsen) and the German Federal Republic. The money from the public sale—360 Million Marks—was brought into a VW-Foundation (Stiftung Volkswagenwerk) to assist in technical and scientific research.

During the years there have been some technical changes. In 1960 a new engine came into being. With 34 bhp, strengthened crankshaft, enlarged bearings, a new fuel-pump drive, improved pushrods, a new carburettor etc. Outwardly the engine did not look much different from the original motor created in 1937, but it had a much improved performance.

Nearly every year customers expected brand new VW cars, but they failed to appear on the market. They still sold well in 1960 and . . . why should they be changed? They were very reliable, economical and still quite cheap to buy. They were also always good value, because a 1950 built VW was outwardly—more or less—the same as a 1960 built one. And there was no difficulty in getting cheap spares and good service in villages and towns in all parts of the world.

Still, there was some talk about a 'big' VW which became true on 1 September 1961 with the production of the 'VW 1500' and a Kharmann-Ghia-Coupé with identical 1.5 litre four-cylinder aircooled engines. It produced 45 bhp at 38000 rpm. And in 1961, the 5 millionth VW was built. By now, VW could manu-

million DM, Export 22 thousand million DM, Investments 4.3 thousand million DM and Taxes paid: 4 thousand million DM. The last amount is proof of the value VW has for the German Government. Nineteen-sixty-six saw the foundation of the 'Deutsche Automobile gesellschaft mbH' in conjunction with Daimler-Benz AG with the purpose of a close co-ordination on research and development. The Volkswagen AG now had a capital of 750 Million Marks . . . and there was also a new VW, the 1600 TL 'Fastback'.

A range of new transporters was introduced in 1967 but on 12 April 1968 a grave shock occurred: Professor Dr Heinrich Nordhoff, the dynamic and very capable VW boss died after a short illness at the age of

Left: the 411 saloon of 1972. Although, like the Beetle, this car used an air-cooled flat-four engine, it was a much more refined car. For example, it had a heating system which would switch itself on at a pre-selected time, so as to make the car nice and warm for its driver before he reached the vehicle on a cold and frosty morning!

Right: the Volkswagen light vans have been quite popular. As well as the van and the pickup, there have been many companies converting them into caravanettes

facture over 1 Million vehicles a year. Thanks to costly, but ultra-modern machinery partly imported from the USA and England, thanks also to more factories and a superb organisation.

A year later saw the 'VW-Variant' and the first foreign labourers, who came from Italy. They eventually got their own 'Italian Village', built for them by VW. In the boom year of 1963 every second car exported by Germany came from VW. There were also new models; the VW 1500S as a limousine, Variant and Coupé. 1964 saw the foundation of 'Volkswagen de Mexico, SA de CV' Mexico DF and on 26 October of the same year the German Mail Office got their 25,000th VW. The demand for the Porsche designed cars reaches a new peak and a new factory at Emden is being opened. During 1964 they paid over one thousand million Marks for salaries to workers and office staff.

The 'Auto Union', in pre-1945 days in the eastern part of Germany, moved to West-Germany and became known mainly for their DKW and Audi cars. They eventually also took over the NSU factory, but came later under Mercedes (Daimler-Benz AG) control. On 5 January 1965 Mercedes sold the whole 'Auto Union'—which included Audi and NSU—to VW at Wolfsburg. Until 1969, many 'Beetles' were made at the Ingolstadt 'Auto Union' factory and 1965 also saw the introduction of 'Fridolin', the VW 147 Transporter for the German Mail with bodies made by 'Westfalia' Works.

Some figures at the end of 1964 are interesting to examine; turnover since 1945: 46.7 thousand

69. On 1 May 1968, Dr Kurt Lotz took over the gigantic car factory as successor to Nordhoff. Three months later, the VW 411 appeared on the market. As a middleclass car with two- and four-doors. The new four-cylinder engine had 69 bhp. By November 1969, 15 million VW cars had left the factories. There was also an important distribution-change in Sweden. Scania-Vabis, famous for big lorries, until then also importers of VW products, dropped the import, which was now taken over by the newly founded 'Svenska Volkswagen AB' at Södertälje in Sweden.

Volkswagenwerk AG Wolfsburg and the Porsche GmbH founded on 11 March 1969 a new company for the sale of sportscars, the VW-Porsche Vertriebsgesellschaft. Two months later, VW started building the sixth German VW factory at Salzgitter Beddingen and on 21 August 1969 Auto Union GmbH and the Neckarsulm NSU Motorenwerke AG became the 'Audi NSU Auto Union AG'. As result of it, Volkswagenwerk AG owned 59.5 per cent of the shares of this new Company. Soon afterwards, VW introduced the new VW 411E with an 80 bhp engine and electronic fuel injection.

VW took over the 'Selbstfahrer-Union', in 1970, the largest rent-a-car firm, and introduced the VW K70. Originally designed by the Neckarsulm NSU works, the K70 was acquired, when VW bought a large part of NSU shares. Needless to say, the K70 was a sensational departure from previous VW designs. It was the very first car with a watercooled engine ever built by VW! Mass production com-

menced in the autumn of 1970 with two engine versions, 75 bhp and 90 bhp. The K70 was an up-to-date design and already had a good reputation before it went into manufacture.

Another car, built by the VW Auto Union factory at Ingolstadt, the Audi 100 was at that time a best-seller. It sold in such quantities, that many of these cars had to be assembled at the Wolfsburg factory, as there was insufficient room for it at Ingolstadt. Without borrowing money from a Bank, VW increased the share capital to 900 million Marks. Business was still very good and even VW of Brasilia had passed the million VW car mark. A new 'Beetle', the VW 1302 with improved suspension units was introduced and 1970 also saw the VW 1302S with a 50 bhp engine on the market.

In comparison with certain foreign sports and small racing cars, running in competition events (but without any assistance from Wolfsburg) with VW-based designs was cheap. Comparatively cheap, because VW parts have been and are cheaper as special parts. In addition, they could be bought in most places in Germany and abroad. And while highly tuned special racing engines proved to be not only expensive, they proved to be also very sensitive. Much more sensitive than tuned VW production engines. While races with such engines as the 498 ccm Jap and Norton single-cylinder became less and less popular, the popularity of races with VW engines increased. Proof was the Formula Five, which came from the USA to Europe and which is now superseded by Formula Super Five.

It was 1963 when a leading German Tuning Company, Oettinger, produced 'Grand Tourisme' versions, homologated by VW. And when the VW 1302S came on the market, it was a perfect car for rebuilding for sporting purposes. Many tuners got over 80 bhp from the Formula Five engines in monoposto racing cars and many famous drivers as Jochen Rindt, Dr Marco, Helmut Koinigg among others drove them with great success. Early in 1971 the first race for Formula Super-Five was at the German Hockenheim-Ring. With engines, of up to 140 bhp and cars made by Bergmann, Fuchs, Royale, Lola, Horag, Motul and other small producers in Germany, Austria, England and other countries. Not bad, if one remembers that the production version of the VW 1302/S has a 1584 cc engine with 50 bhp at 4000 rpm.

'Normal' VW cars still have the Porsche-designed, flat four-cylinder OHV-engine with aircooling in the rear with 1192 ccm, 34 bhp at 3600 rpm and with 1285 ccm, 40 bhp at 4000 rpm. The bigger versions have 1493 ccm and 45 bhp at 3800 rpm and 1584 ccm and 14 bhp at 4000 rpm.

While the 'Beetle' was being improved and new VW cars in the experimental department, a new 'safety' car was created in 1971 partly under pressure from America. By 27 August 1971, five million VWs had been sent to America. But the situation is no longer as rosy as ten years earlier and after some internal reorganisation, Rudolf Leiding, who was until then in charge of VW de Brazil, took over on 1 October the whole VW-Empire at Wolfsburg. Not an easy task, if one takes in account the 170,000 employees of the car giant. On 17 February 1972 the VW car number 15,007,034 was produced to take the lead of the list of cars with the largest production figure. Until then it had been Henry Fords model 'T'. And in August 1972 the VW 1303 succeeded the 1302.

For pure sporting activities, two cars entered the field in the early seventies: the VW-Porsche 914/6 and

Above: the first of a new breed of cars from Volkswagen, the K70L front-wheel-drive, water-cooled saloon

Below: the uprated 411 engine provided power for the Volks-Porsche 914

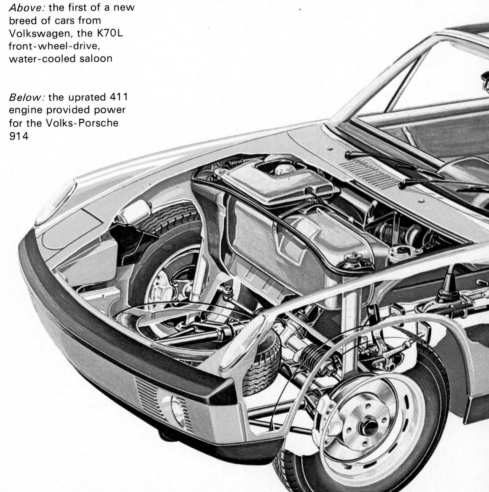

the 914-2.0. The first one, built at the Porsche factory, had a 1991 cc 6-cylinder double-ohc engine with aircooling and 110 bhp and 5800 rpm in the back, the 2-litre car a four-cylinder 1971 cc aircooled engine with push-rods and 100 bhp at 5000 rpm. The 'Six' took 9.9 seconds to reaching 100 km/h and had a top speed of over 200 km/h; the 'Four' could do 100 km/h in 9.6 seconds and go 196 km/h.

The sensation of 1973 was the introduction of the 'Passat'. A sensation, because it left the old VW-tradition by having front-wheel-drive and a four-cylinder in-line engine as well as a self-supporting steel body. It was obtainable with 55 bhp, 75 bhp and 85 bhp engines. Meanwhile, the good old Volkswagen 'Beetle' was still very much alive and far from obsolete. It continued to sell to a loyal public in very good, if declining numbers.

And while the VW 'Beetle' has been built for so many years without great design changes, its successors—although of up-to-date specifications—will not have such long lives because the whole world structure has changed since the introduction of the 'peoples-car'. The Beetle came on the market when there was a great shortage of cars everywhere. It was the right car at the right time. Now, new Volkswagen cars face ever increasing competition in nearly all the countries of the world. Therefore, more models for a wider circle of customers have been introduced. Among them, the 'Scirocco' is a four-seater with a two-door coupé by Kharmann and obtainable with the 50 bhp, 70 bhp or the 85 bhp transversely mounted engines. It was introduced during the petrol shortage and decreasing car sales of February 1974.

Three months afterwards, the 'real' successor to the old 'Beetle', the 'Golf' was introduced to the Press. It is now being produced on the old production lines, while the original VW is made at the Hannover, Emden and Bruxelles factories only.

Gone are the days when VW had only one model. In 1974, after over 18 million VW cars had left the production lines since World War II, they could offer twenty basic models, several of which no longer had any connection with the basic design created by old prof. Porsche who died soon after his 75th birthday in January 1951.

The—so far—newest VW is the 1974 Golf with 1093 cc and the Golf S with 1471 cc four-cylinder engine and frontwheel drive. A car, which is entirely different from the original VW conception. Gone is the aircooled engine in the rear, gone the drive to the rearwheels. The Golf has a traditional engine in the front with water-cooling and the four cylinders in line. Different also is the situation as far as sales are concerned. For many years, VW had difficulties in producing sufficient cars, as the demand was exceptionally big. The Golf, successor to the 'Beetle', came into being when most car factories in the world had fantastic numbers of new cars on their stocks. Still, it soon gained great popularity and sold well. Comparatively well. The question remains open, if it ever will sell as well as the Beetle; and in such quantities over so many years as the Beetle. Even VW has had to cut down production and the number of their employees.

Late 1974, with the VW personnel already cut down from about 150,000 to 115,000, the Wolfsburg Empire was in great difficulties and just when writing these lines, important changes on the highest levels of the factory are being made. And while 20 years ago customers were 'fighting' for every VW 'Beetle', VW is now fighting for every buyer of a Golf, Passat or Scirocco.   ET

GOLF 1500LS

The Italians are renowned for their flamboyant design, both in their multi-camshaft V12 engines and in their elegant bodies. The Germans, however, are the practical ones; making neat, well engineered cars. One might think, if ever the two styles got together in one car, there would be an awful clash of styles.

But that was not the case when Volkswagen commissioned Giorgetto Giugiaro's Ital Design to style the bodies for several of their front-wheel-drive, water-cooled cars, however.

The smallest of the cars designed, up until the arrival of the mini Polo, was the Golf, available in several engine-size options and as either two- or four-door. Apart from the high-performance GTI, with a 1600 cc 110 bhp fuel injected engine, the top of the range is the 1500LS five-door car.

The car's engine is a 1471 cc belt-driven-overhead-camshaft unit that produces 70 bhp and 83 lb ft of torque. These give a top speed of just on 100 mph and enable the 1500LS to accelerate from 0–50 mph in 9 secs.

All the power can be used most of the time in the neat, buzzy little car as it handles and corners superbly by way of its all-round independent suspension, front-wheel drive and grippy tyres.

Practicality is also a forte: there is a large tailgate that provides access to the rear boot and, if necessary, the rear seat folds down to provide an exceptionally large luggage platform.

ENGINE Front-mounted, water-cooled straight-four slanted at 20° to the rear. 76.5 mm (3.01 in) bore × 80 mm (3.15 in) stroke = 1471 cc (89.8 cu in). Maximum power (DIN) 70 bhp at 5800 rpm; maximum torque (DIN) 83 lb ft at 3000 rpm. Cast-iron cylinder block and light-alloy head. Compression ratio 8.2:1. 5 main bearings. 2 valves per cylinder operated, via thimble tappets, by a single belt-driven overhead camshaft. 1 Solex downdraught single-barrel carburettor.

TRANSMISSION Single-dry-plate clutch and four-speed manual gearbox, or torque converter and three-speed automatic unit. Ratios for manual, 1st 3.454, 2nd 1.960, 3rd 1.370, 4th 0.970, rev 3.170:1. Ratios for automatic, 1st 2.550, 2nd 1.450, 3rd 1, rev 2.410:1. Maximum ratio of converter at stall 2.44. Spiral-bevel final drive. Ratio 3.900 (manual), or 3.760 (automatic).

CHASSIS Integral.

SUSPENSION Front—independent by MacPherson struts, coil springs and lower wishbones, rear—independent by swinging longitudinal trailing arms, linked by a T-section cross beam, coil springs and telescopic dampers.

STEERING Rack and pinion.

BRAKES Servo-assisted front discs and rear drums.

WHEELS 5 in × 13 in steel.

TYRES 155SR × 13.

DIMENSIONS AND WEIGHT Wheelbase 94.49 in; track—front 54.72 in, rear—53.54 in; length 145.67 in; width 63.39 in; height 55.51 in; ground clearance 4.92 in; dry weight 1720 lb; turning circle between walls 34 ft; fuel tank capacity 9.9 gals.

BODY 5-door, 4–5-seater.

PERFORMANCE Maximum speed 100 mph. Acceleration 0–50 mph 9 secs. Fuel consumption approximately 30 mpg.

SCIROCCO

The cars that Giorgetto Guigero created for Volkswagen were fundamentally practical in design and appearance—one thinks of the Golf and the Passat.

In the Scirocco, though, Ital Design produced a car that was only slightly less practical than its stablemates, yet much more in the flowing, Italian style.

Available in various engine sizes on the home, German market, the car was available in Britain with just the 85 bhp 1471 cc unit. At the Frankfurt show in September 1975, though, a new car with a 1588 cc engine was announced. This power unit gave the same bhp figure as the older version (85 bhp), but its torque figure of 89 lb ft was raised to 92 lb ft at 600 rpm.

The car uses the same all-independent suspension layout as the Golf, with MacPherson struts, coil springs and lower wishbones at the front, and swinging longitudinal trailing arms, linked by a T-section cross beam, coil springs and telescopic dampers at the rear. With this neat layout, front-wheel drive and 175-section tyres, the roadholding is exceptional.

The three-door car, with tartan-cloth seat inserts matching exterior paint finish, in new form has a single wiper to sweep the windscreen and, as is popular, another wiper and washer for the rear.

Finally, like all Volkswagens, there is a little plastic box under the bonnet containing plug sockets. When the car is to be serviced, the mechanic plugs the car into an analyser which automatically traces any faults.

ENGINE Front-mounted, water-cooled straight-four angled at 20° to the rear. 79.5 mm (3.13 in) bore × 80 mm (3.15 in) stroke = 1588 cc (96.9 cu in). Maximum power (DIN) 85 bhp at 5800 rpm; maximum torque (DIN) 92 lb ft at 3800 rpm. Compression ratio 9.7:1. Cast-iron cylinder block and light-alloy head. 5 main bearings. 2 valves per cylinder operated, via thimble tappets, by a single belt-driven overhead camshaft. 1 Solex downdraught single-barrel carburettor.

TRANSMISSION Single-dry-plate clutch and 4-speed manual gearbox. Ratios, 1st 3.450, 2nd 1.960, 3rd 1.370, 4th 0.970, rev 3.170:1. Spiral-bevel final drive. Ratio 3.900.

CHASSIS Integral.

SUSPENSION Front—independent by MacPherson struts, coil springs and lower wishbones, rear—independent by swinging longitudinal trailing arms, linked by a T-section cross beam, coil springs and telescopic dampers.

STEERING Rack and pinion.

BRAKES Servo-assisted front discs and rear drums.

WHEELS 5 in × 13 in light-alloy.

TYRES 175/70 SR × 13.

DIMENSIONS AND WEIGHT Wheelbase 94.49 in; track—front 54.72 in, rear—53.15 in; length 152.36 in; width 63.78 in; height 51.57 in; ground clearance 4.92 in; dry weight 1720 lb; turning circle between walls 33.6 ft; fuel tank capacity 9.9 gals.

BODY 3-door, 4-seater coupé.

PERFORMANCE Maximum speed 113 mph. Acceleration 0–50 mph 7.4 secs. Fuel consumption approximately 30 mpg.

THE FOUNDER OF SWEDEN'S MOTOR INDUSTRY

Sweden's foremost car company evolved into the world's foremost manufacturers of 'safety cars'

Above: a 1928 version of Volvo's first car, the ÖV4; this car featured a four-cylinder side-valve engine of 1944 cc

SCANDINAVIA'S LARGEST INDUSTRIAL UNDERTAKING was born over a dish of crayfish in a Stockholm restaurant in 1924. Two Swedish engineers, Assar Gabrielsson and Gustaf Larson, who had been colleagues in the big SKF ball-bearing firm, decided over their seafood meal that Sweden ought to have a car industry. Larson had worked for some years in the British car industry, and was able to contribute design. Gabrielsson, sales manager at SKF, had management expertise to offer. An artist called Helmer Mas-Olle tackled styling.

All they needed was money. Even without financial backing the team pooled their resources to produce a series of ten prototypes, the first of which was ready by June 1926 and promptly made a successful run from Stockholm to Gothenburg. This effort attracted the attention of SKF, who took a very short while to decide to back these pioneers. SKF even had a small subsidiary company which they handed over as a ready-made manufacturing concern. It was called Volvo—based on the Latin for 'I roll', a reference to rolled steel. Gabrielsson and Larson became the

chief executives, and Volvo was in business to manufacture cars.

From the start it was decided to utilise the capacity of the Swedish engineering industry, with the manufacture of components by various Swedish companies and assembly by Volvo at Gothenburg. It was a modest enough beginning—a mere ten workers assembled the first model, nicknamed Jacob. On 14 April 1927, model ÖV4, was completed, with an open sheet-steel body on a frame of ash and red beech, and a four-cylinder side-valve 1944 cc engine giving 28 bhp and a top speed of 48 mph. After an embarrassing technical hitch whereby the car would run only in reverse gear, the Jacob rolled out of the factory gate. In all 205 were built.

The following year another version appeared, the PV4, with the same chassis and running gear but with a closed wooden leatherette-clad body. In 1928 a 'Special' was added, with a fuller specification. It drew attention to Volvo internationally by winning its class in a Moscow-Leningrad-Moscow speed, economy and reliability trial. It was well built and sold steadily, taking total Volvo production into four figures.

In 1929 a six-cylinder car was produced, the PV650, with a 68 mph capability from its 55 bhp 3010 cc engine. It soon went into PV651 and 652 series with hydraulic brakes and a synchronised gearbox. Production of this car displaced the earlier four-cylinder models and 2400 were made. A TR670 wooden-frame model, and similar TR671–674 models but with seven-seater taxi bodies, were added to the range, which was produced until 1934, some 600 being built.

During the 1930s Volvo evolved a series of solid family cars somewhat similar in appearance to the American cars of the period. The PV653 and 654 saloons and PV655 luxury version with wooden frame, two spare wheels and automatic reversing lights were produced in 1933 and 1934. These models offered five seats and were powered by a 65 bhp 3266 cc six-cylinder side-valve engine driving through a three-speed gearbox with freewheel facility.

Ever mindful of the working nature of the motor car Volvo followed on with three taxi versions of this car, the TR676, TR678 and TR679 models, with two occasional seats between front and rear seats extending the seating capacity to seven. TR675 and TR677 models of the same series were separate-frame prototypes of which only a couple were built in 1934.

A steady rounding of the body style was in evidence with the return to the PV series in 1935. The PV658 and 659 saloons were based on the previous PV cars but had a bigger six-cylinder unit displacing 3670 cc and producing 80/84 bhp. The bonnet was lengthening now and the radiator inclined slightly rearwards. The total appearance was similar to the Chrysler Airflow model of the same time. Production of these five-seaters continued until 1937, more than 400 being made. As usual, taxis were also based on these models, with three versions produced. All had seven-seater bodies and more than 900 were built—further evidence that Volvo favoured the business user rather than the private owner. A run of separate-framed TR702 models to order during these two years totalled only eleven cars.

The emphasis changed in the mid-thirties however. Having assuaged the taxi market with its Big Sixes, Volvo settled with the 3670 cc engine for an extensive series of PV models which carried the firm up to, through and beyond World War II. It began with the PV36 of 1935—Volvo's first streamlined model with faired-in headlamps, known as the Carioca. It had a steel body, excellent comfort levels, and featured independent front suspension. Five-hundred were built.

It was followed in 1936 by PV51 and 52, which stepped back a bit by having separate headlamps. Its spaciousness, good road-holding and economy made it Sweden's most popular car, and about 3000 were produced between 1936 and 1938.

Two larger wheelbase taxi models with eight-seater bodies (including three occasional seats) and up to 86 bhp output from the same engine were brought out in 1938. More than 1600 of these were built up to 1947. Despite their size they handled easily and remained a familiar sight on Sweden's streets until the late 1950s.

Volvo was one of the very few car makers able to think in terms of new models during the early 1940s, and in 1942 devised a new six-seater saloon, the PV60, using the same engine and three-speed transmission but with the innovation of optional overdrive. Five of these cars were built in 1942, the car was publicly announced two years later, and production commenced in 1946, continuing until 1950. Just over

3000 were built. This was the last of the 'Americanised' Volvos, and also the last six-cylinder Volvo until 1968.

The version of the 3670 cc engine installed in this car, which produced 90 bhp, was also used in the first Volvo post-war taxis, the PV821 and 822 models of 1947 and 1948. The frontal treatment of these departed from the separate headlamp style, with a strong horizontal grille treatment linking the front wings and the headlamps placed well in from the corners of the car to protect them from incidental damage. About 500 of these cars were built, and at the time Sweden regarded them as the perfect taxi. A further 1100 autos in another series, the PV831 and 832 used the same body and components but with some refinements were produced from 1950 to 1957 From 1950 to 1958 two related saloons sharing the same body and running gear were produced more than 2000 of which went to private owners.

But as far back as 1944 Volvo management had looked ahead to a post-war demand for smaller and more economical cars, and developed a small saloon with a 1414 cc overhead valve four-cylinder engine

Top: a prototype for the ÖV4; as in the production versions, the car used a sheet-metal body over a frame built of ash and red beach. The first cars were nicknamed Jacob

Above: the PV4 Special of 1928; this car used the same frame as the ÖV4, but featured a leatherette-clad saloon-type body

developing 44 bhp. This PV444 model, with a two-door integral steel body, independent front suspension, coil rear suspension, three-speed gearbox and hydraulic brakes was the first Volvo to sell in any quantity outside Scandinavia, and it rapidly established for Volvo an international reputation for solid quality construction and good manners.

The basic PV444 design remained in production for fourteen years, though eight substantial series of improvements were rendered, including one uprating of power output from 44 to 51 bhp and, finally, the enlargement of engine capacity to 1583 cc and the output to 60 bhp. Altogether the PV444 production totalled 196,000 up to 1958. From 1953 to 1960 a related PV445 in a total of 22 versions was also produced, although in much smaller numbers. These included a number of pick-up and van versions.

Volvo tried a brief departure from the serious working-car approach in 1956/7 in the form of the P1900, an open sports car with glassfibre body fitted with a 70 bhp version of the PV 1414 cc engine, and capable of 108 mph. This car was intended for export only, though a few were sold in Sweden. Only 67 were built.

In 1958 everyone thought Volvo were going to drop the long-running PV444 design—but they did so only in favour of a thoroughly revised car, the PV544,

which bore a close family resemblance to the 444. In the seven years of its life it had seven revisions. For the first three years it was powered by a 76 bhp version of the 1583 cc engine, then this unit was uprated further to 1778 cc and 90 bhp. In its final two-door PV544 form this engine gave 95 bhp. When production ceased in 1965, 440,000 units of this car had been produced.

Over the same period five versions of a 544-based van or estate, the Duett 210, were produced, firstly with a separate chassis framework and later with an integral steel body. After the end of 544 production the Duett continued until 1969, and a total of 61,000 of these vehicles was produced between 1960 and 1969.

Overlapping with the best-selling PV544 series, a new and decidedly modern large saloon came into being, starting in 1956 with the P1200, a four-door saloon with a vertically split grille and a broad-shouldered body style that carried the Volvo badge into new market areas. Powered by the proven 1583 cc 444 engine putting out 60 bhp, it was marketed as the 120. Nearly 13,000 of these were made, and in 1958 came modifications which resulted in 121 and 122 versions. The latter was the model that really made Volvo familiar in Britain. Over the period from 1956 to 1966 no fewer than seventeen versions with this bodyshell were produced, including upratings of the

1583 cc engine to give 85 bhp, and the adoption in 1961 of the previous 1778 cc engine of the 544 which was still in production for the home market at that time. A two-door P130 version was added in 1961 and ran through to 1970, embracing in 1968 a further increase in engine size to 1986 cc and an output of 118 bhp. A total of 564,000 of this important series were produced.

Scarcely less important, at least in the British market, was the related P220 series—the estate version. It was the estate car more than any other vehicle that introduced Volvo to a wide British public. It was unchallenged in its market sector, became a firm favourite with doctors and other professional people, and earned Volvo a massive reputation as the producer of tough, reliable and long-lasting cars.

The P220 estates appeared in 1962. They underwent seven sets of modification—improvement was an annual affair at Volvo—and a total of 72,000 were produced up to 1969.

While the 120/121/122/130 saloons and 220 estates were putting Volvo into the big league, however, they were also establishing something else—Volvo's pre-occupation with car safety. In 1956 the 120 pioneered a safety steering column with shear coupling. Rear seat belt anchorages followed in 1958, and front seat belts became a production-line fitting in 1959.

In 1962 Volvo was fitting large-diameter disc brakes on all four wheels. A brake servo and pressure limiting valve on the rear brakes to prevent locking up and skidding were added in 1965. The firm also acquired a reputation for thinking of the customer's backs—the seating, from 1964, was highly adjustable and orthopaedically correct.

Though the 120/130 series soldiered on until 1970, in 1966 a totally new body appeared—the 144 four-door, supplemented the following year by the 142 two-door and the 145 estate. These models in their various forms—were powered by 1778 cc or 1986 cc versions of the well-tried four-cylinder unit. It was in Volvo's approach to their construction that they were most significant, however.

Notable was the body construction—impact-absorbing front and rear compartments developed with the use of crash-testing, and a near crush-proof passenger compartment incorporating a roll-over bar in the roof structure, and anti-burst door locks. This great body strength was only one half of the story, for Volvo also devised a dual-circuit fail-safe braking system—discs all round with a double split-triangle system, each linking both front wheel brakes with one rear. These, and several other detail safety features such as a new telescopic steering column, anticipated forthcoming legislation and marked Volvo as showing the way whereby logic could and should be applied to car construction rather than allow the old conventions and attitudes to continue. This approach was to become more and more important as critics of the motor car in general turned on the car makers and accused them of anti-social attitudes, and even of negligence and careless-

Above: no fewer than 440,000 of these PV544s, based on the PV444, were manufactured between 1958 and 1965

Below: the 122S of 1967

ness with the safety of their customers.

More than this—further improvements introduced by Volvo, such as front head restraints and a heated rear screen as standard equipment in 1969 and rear window wash-wipe in the 1970 estate, pointed the way eventually followed by every car manufacturer. These innovations demonstrated that so-called luxury items on expensive cars were not luxuries at all but important features affecting the driving safety of every motorist and by no means the prerogative of the wealthy.

The 142/144/145 series of four-cylinder cars which set the seal on Volvo's total involvement with safety was joined in 1968 by the 164, the firm's first six-cylinder car since the PB60. With leather upholstery and automatic seat-belts among its standard fitments the 164 rapidly became the top-selling six-cylinder car in its home market, and did well in export markets too, again benefitting from Volvo's increasing stature as a builder of enormously strong and safe cars. Again there was an annual revision, and up to 1974 production of this 2978 cc 164 had totalled 134,000.

Though the 142/144/145 four-cylinder range was replaced in 1974, the 164 remained successful in the market place.

While the 120 series was thriving through the 1960s, Volvo again tried its hand at a sports car, and the fixed-head GT two-seater P1800 was announced in 1961, utilising the same 1778 cc unit firstly in its 100 bhp form, and later in 108 and 115 bhp forms. This engine was also employed briefly at the time by Facel Vega and Marcos. The P1800 bodies were built for Volvo by Jensen at West Bromwich. Some 28,000 of these were produced up to 1968, when the 1986 cc unit was fitted, firstly in 118 bhp tune and then in 130 and finally 135 bhp form. Another 10,000 of this model were produced with these engines before the model was discontinued in 1972. From 1971 to 1973 a sporting-estate 1800 in the Reliant GTE manner was produced, using the 135 bhp engine. More than 8000 were built.

Volvo's commitment to greater structural integrity and safety design in cars crystallised in 1969, when the firm established its own criteria for an experimental safety vehicle. A fleet of ten of these 'rolling safety laboratories' was to be built. These were to be no theoretical vehicles, however. While the American safety vehicle requirements published in 1970 (and surprisingly similar to Volvo's own list) resulted in a number of armoured and overweight vehicles which would have smashed anything they nudged and guzzled fuel whenever they turned a wheel, Volvo were aiming for practical application of the results of their experiment.

The Volvo ESVs (experimental safety vehicles) combined all that Volvo had so far devised and incorporated into the 144 series, with other safety design already planned for the next series. The result was one large safety project that related to existing Volvo cars, and was therefore at the same time a production project. Different ESV's in the fleet featured different ideas, but the definitive vehicle added something like a score of positive safety improvements to the already well-wrought 144 structure. More than 40 inches of deformation were designed in for frontal crashes of up to 50 mph. Front and rear bumpers were rubber faced, the ends sheathed in moulded plastic to prevent their hooking into anything, and mounted on telescoping shock absorbers so that the front bumper would flex seven inches in a 10 mph bump and the rear 3½ inches. The grille sloped to deflect any unfortunate person struck by the front of the car. The headlamps were well sunk, and provided with a wash and wiper system. Brakes, discs all round, were fitted with an electronically controlled anti-lock system, and radial ply tyres were fitted for longer life and better roadholding. The rear suspension had a self-levelling system.

The screenwipers were recessed so that a pedestrian flung on to the bonnet by the sloping grille would not be torn by the wiper arms. Hooked door-lock units were installed to prevent doors bursting open in a crash. In any type of collision at least two doors

were designed to remain openable to allow rescuers into the car.

A protective side moulding ran all the way round the bodywork to guard against incidental bodywork damage. Tubular reinforcement members were mounted laterally inside the doors to minimise the risk of intrusion by another vehicle hitting the side of the car—no more than four inches intrusion from another 30 mph vehicle. Doubled steel members were built into the window pillars and a doubled steel rollover bar was incorporated into the roof.

In all types of accident the entire fuel system was designed to remain intact, with a deceleration-

activated cutout fuel pump positioned towards the rear to minimise the risk of petrol spillage and fire. Fire retardant materials were specified for the interior.

The interior was stripped of all protrusions and padding was employed generously. Automatic three-point seat belts were installed. Head restraints popped up on the front seats in a collision. The backs of the front seats were thickly padded to minimise the risk of injury to rear passengers flung forwards in an impact. Rear seat head restraints were installed. The feel of the car was lightened and made more sensitive than in the weighty 144 series, and a spring-loaded steering wheel was fitted so that in the event of a frontal crash the steering wheel was instantly jerked six inches forward to the facia and at the same time away from the driver.

In some Volvo ESV's air bags were installed. Others had door-mounted seat belts, and others a semi-passive design which came into operation automatically when the car was started and the handbrake released. Various systems were tried to ensure that a disproportionately heavy load in the rear did not cause the headlamp alignment to dazzle oncoming traffic.

And all the ESV's featured four-cylinder fuel-injection engines equipped with exhaust gas re-circulation systems and catalytic converters for maximum pollution control.

Volvo was not the only car maker experimenting with safety at this time, but the firm certainly took things further earlier than any other European manufacturer, and the strictly practical attitude to its findings found expression in 1974 with the appearance of the 144 series replacements—the 242 two-door saloon, the 244 four-door, the 245 estate car and the 264 four-door. These cars are expected to take Volvo into the 1980s. The 242/244/245 are powered by a new four-cylinder 2127 cc engine with crossflow aluminium alloy cylinder head and belt-driven overhead camshaft. This engine appears in two forms: with 8.5 to 1 compression ratio giving 97 bhp at 5000 rpm, and with 9.3 to 1 compression ratio produc-

Below left: the estate-car version of the 120 series was known as the 220; this car was in production between 1962 and 1969

Top: made famous by the English TV series *The Saint* was this P1800S of 1964

Above right: a 1967 144S, the car which was to provide Volvos base production right into the 1970s

Above: here, a Volvo 142 is seen on the Swedish rally; these cars have been quite successful in rallying events in Scandinavia

ing 123 bhp at 5750 rpm. But both accept economical 93 octane petrol.

The 264 is fitted with a new 90-degree V6 unit displacing 2664 cc's, with aluminium alloy engine block with wet liners, aluminium cylinder heads, and a chain-driven overhead camshaft between the valves on each bank. Ignition is of the transistorised breaker-less type, and the fuel system is continuous-injection, these systems allowing a high standard of emission control with settings remaining accurate over a long period. This engine also uses 93 octane fuel. Output is 140 bhp at 6000 rpm with a compression ratio of 8.7 to 1.

But while Volvo have moved into a new generation of engines, they have also utilised the knowledge which their ESV programme produced. For instance, the 200 series, incorporating basically the same telescopic bumper and frontal deformation principles perfected in the experimental cars, meet at 40 mph the American requirements for a 30 mph frontal collision, though the 40 mph crash creates almost double the kinetic energy as the 30 mph one. This characteristic alone has reduced the stresses on occupants by 20 per cent compared with the 140 cars.

Further innovations have come in 1975—notably 'day-notice' lights which come on automatically with

the ignition and stay on to help other traffic perceive the car's approach: a stepped-bore master-cylinder giving almost full braking effect without increased pedal load with one brake cylinder out of operation: and rear seat belts as standard.

The sum total of these safety characteristics, the need for many of which Volvo identified as much by accident analysis as by its own controlled experiments, has led the firm to claim that the 200 series cars are the world's first PSV's—production safety vehicles. Many authorities would not dispute the claim—the day-notice lights and stepped-bore master cylinder won the Swedish AA Gold Medal in 1975, Spain gave the 200 series the Velocidad award for its safety provisions, an Italian Gold Medal was awarded as a result of a readers' poll in fourteen daily newspapers to find the car maker with the best reputation for products and services, a leading Norwegian magazine chose the 244 as Car of the Year for its safety, life-expectancy and trade-in value, and America's top motoring magazine chose the 244 as the best family car in all categories in competition with 45 other models.

A new small Volvo was added to the range this year —the 66GL, based on the current DAF saloon and estate and powered by the Renault 1300 unit, but with the interior redesigned by Fiore and a radical revision of the Variomatic transmission. In 1974 and 1975 Volvo bought a controlling interest in the DAF car operation and established its own operation, Volvo Car BV, at Eindhoven, so resolving the firm's long-standing intention of getting into the smaller car market segment, though the DAF has been used as a basis for the first model, an entirely new medium car is due in 1976, designed by Fiore.

Meanwhile the Volvo 66 has brought to the DAF-based two-door profile the familiar Volvo preoccupation with safety—telescopic steering shaft, inertia belts front and rear, front seat head restraints, split brake circuits, high-impact laminated screen, and rubber-faced bumpers. The overhead-valve engine produces 57 bhp at 5200 rpm. Brakes are power-assisted, the fronts being discs. The DAF De Dion rear axle is retained.

One cannot leave the Volvo car scene without referring to the work methods which the firm helped (with Saab) to pioneer, and which are often considered to be a significant factor in Volvo quality and reliability. The company's car assembly plant at Kalmar has become a landmark in the use of technology to eliminate assembly lines as such and to increase the job-satisfaction of the employees.

Kalmar grew in the early 70's out of a joint project by management under the newly-appointed managing director Pehr Gyllenhammar and labour representatives from all levels. They had as a working brief the experiences of Volvo at various of its other plants where ongoing efforts had been made to achieve a better

port unit and working platform for the bodies during assembly (it can turn the bodies through 90 degrees on to their sides for easier working), the carrier also functions as a transmitter of information to the factory's four computers which control overall production and monitor quality. Volvo safety design has even played a part in these carriers—they have spring-loaded bumpers sensitive to a collision, and will stop from maximum speed within eight centimeters.

Volvo later tackled engine assembly in the same way, and in 1974 opened a new engine plant at Skövda employing groups of workers and assembly carriers instead of line assembly. Highly mechanised handling and electronic control of machining has meant that women are in no way precluded from the traditionally laborious engine shops. Women will have about 40 per cent of the 1000 jobs when Skövda is on full

working environment for employer and employee.

The result at Kalmar was a new approach on both technical and social levels. The atmosphere of a small workshop was achieved by sub-dividing assembly into twenty-five separate team operations, each group consisting of about fifteen people, with further sub-division into groups of two or three for certain types of job. The transport of bodies is on separate battery-driven assembly carriers, not production lines, so that greater freedom in work planning is a basic fact. In consultation with the foreman and production engineer the workers themselves suggest the working plan and division of responsibility for various operations, and job rotation is a feature of work patterns. In addition to assembly work, the workers are also responsible for materials supplies in their own team area and they play a part in continuous quality inspection. Work rates and breaks are varied to suit team and individual needs and wishes.

Core of the system is the assembly carrier, devised by Volvo, and controlled through electrical impulses from cables concealed in the floor. As well as a trans-

stream, producing 275,000 engines a year.

Kalmar and Skövda are new factories, and innovations was comparatively easy, but Volvo has also been tackling improvement at its older plants, and at the huge ten year-old Torslanda works at Gothenburg nearly a quarter of the 8000 workers have chosen to learn new tasks so that they can take part in job rotation.

A major factor in Volvo's success has of course been the diversity of its activities as Scandinavia's largest industrial group. While its cars have provided it with a familiar public face, its twenty-seven Swedish factories and twelve whole or partly-owned factories outside its home country also produce trucks, buses, marine and industrial engines, earth-moving, forestry and agricultural machinery, and jet engines for the Swedish air force. Worldwide, Volvo employs 51,400 people, and the group's products are sold in 120 countries, 70 per cent of turnover being in exports.

This traffic is not all one-way however. Volvo's car operation buys many components in Britain, £50 million worth in 1974.   EF

Above: the 1973 Volvo VESC (Volvo's Experimental Safety Car) is a rolling laboratory for the testing of safety systems; some of the items on this car have been incorporated into later models, like the nose and front-light layout for the 240 series. However, this car has some safety features that may not be seen on production cars. They include air bags, for all passengers and 'pop-up' head restraints

245

For a great part of the 1960s, the Volvo 140 series of cars had held a reputation of being rugged, reliable and safe.

When, in August 1974, the 240 series was announced they were just as rugged, more reliable (the mileometer read to 999,999 miles!) and had many more safety features: the first thing one notices is the protection afforded by the car's massive '5 mph' bumpers.

The older 140s used pushrod engines, but the later 240s utilise the B21 overhead-camshaft 2.1-litre engines. In the 245, it is in single-carburetted form producing 97 bhp and 125 lb ft of torque. This power gives the car a top speed of 98 mph and accelerate it to 60 mph from rest in 13 secs. Fuel consumption to the order of 22 mpg is returned from the 26 cwt car.

MacPherson strut front suspension is used, while a live-axle rear layout suspends the rear of the big estate. In normal form, the 245 can hold five large adults. A useful extra is the fold-up seat that fits in the luggage platform facing rearwards that can hold up to three small children.

Although the car's handling is not in the sports-car class, the roadholding is adequate if not inspiring and the performance is hardly that of a racer, one must respect that the 245 is one of the largest European estate cars made, one of the safest cars to travel in and one that will last a long time. Taken in that context, rather than as a sports car, the big Volvo has few equals.

ENGINE Front-mounted, water-cooled straight-four. 92 mm (3.62 in) bore × 80 mm (3.15 in) stroke = 2127 cc (130 cu in). Maximum power (DIN) 97 bhp at 5000 rpm; maximum torque (DIN) 125 lb ft at 2500 rpm. Cast-iron cylinder block and light-alloy head. Compression ratio 8.5:1. 5 main bearings. 2 valves per cylinder operated direct by a single overhead camshaft. 1 Zenith Stromberg CD 175 semi-downdraught carburettor.

TRANSMISSION Single-dry-plate clutch and four-speed manual gearbox. Ratios, 1st 3.41, 2nd 1.99, 3rd 1.36, 4th 1, rev 3.25:1. Hypoid-bevel final drive. Ratio 3.9:1.

CHASSIS Integral.

SUSPENSION Front—independent by MacPherson struts, an anti-roll bar, coil springs and telescopic dampers, rear—non-independent by a rigid axle, located by trailing links and a Panhard rod, coil springs and telescopic dampers.

STEERING Rack and pinion. Turns from lock to lock 4.3.

BRAKES Dual-circuit servo-assisted discs all round.

WHEELS 5 in × 14 in steel.

TYRES 185SR × 14.

Wheelbase 104 in; track—front 56 in, rear—53 in; length 192.08 in; width 67.3 in; height 57.5 in; ground clearance 7.3 in; dry weight 2912 lb; turning circle between walls 30 ft; fuel tank capacity 13.2 gals.

BODY Estate car, five-door five seats. Extra three-child seat optional for luggage platform.

PERFORMANCE Maximum speed 98 mph. Acceleration 0–60 mph 13 secs. Fuel consumption 22 mpg.

SOUTHPORT'S GOD OF FIRE

As with many other companies, like Dennis, Thornycroft and Maudslay, Vulcan were better known for their commercials

Right: a 1910 Vulcan 12 hp near the entrance of a Hindu temple in Madras

FEW CARS HAVE BEEN ADVERTISED by a snappy cross-talk act: but the Vulcan Motor & Engineering Company was obviously of the opinion that their products could be sold by the sort of unconvincing dialogue usually reserved for toothpaste advertising. 'Float along in comfort in the Vulcan 12 Saloon,' burbled a 1925 ad: and then came the hard (?) sell. . . .

Peter: 'It's luxury motoring for me, my boy—I'm out for comfort, and I have it in the Vulcan 12 Saloon.

Paul: I believe quite a lot can be said for the saloon body in this variable climate of ours. After all, an ordinary car has its hood up two-thirds of its life—especially if one indulges in night riding.

Peter: Just so; and, of course, one must take care of the ladies. In the Vulcan Saloon, they are as warm and cosy as in the drawing room at home—they float along in comfort without jar or vibration even over bumpy roads. The Vulcan 12 is very easy to handle on the road, most comfortable to ride in, and the engine runs beautifully.

Paul: It certainly is a handsome turnout. I wish luxury motoring were within my means.

Peter: Why, man, of course it is. The Vulcan 12 Saloon is only the price of an ordinary open car—the year's tax is but £12, and depreciation on any Vulcan is less than on many cars I know. Let me give you a lift home, then you'll know the delights of real luxury motoring.

But it wasn't 'real luxury motoring' which made the name of the Vulcan. The company, based in Southport, Lancashire, was more famous for its commercial vehicles than for its cars. Mind you, the first experimental Vulcan cars had appeared a long time before, in 1897–99, the work of Thomas and Joseph Hampson.

The marque reached production status in 1902, when a 4 hp 'Motor Phaeton' was shown at the Agricultural Hall Show. Priced at 130 guineas, it had a single-cylinder engine, apparently of Vulcan's own make, and single belt drive to the back axle, which incorporated a three-speed gear, probably of the epicyclic type, inside the belt pulley.

A 6 hp of more substantial design appeared the following year, then came a 10 hp twin-cylinder model. This had a swept volume of 1342 cc, and was to survive in production until 1909. A brace of four-cylinder models made their début in 1905: these were a 12/14 hp of 2212 cc and a 16 hp of 3191 cc. The company was reformed in 1906, in which year the range was enlarged by the addition of a 14 hp model, with a swept volume of 2737 cc, which soon supplanted the 12/14 hp, and a 20 hp four of 3922 cc. At the Olympia Motor Show Vulcan's first six-cylinder model appeared; its 30 hp engine had a capacity of 4786 cc. It lasted only one season, and was then replaced by a 35 hp with an enlarged bore giving a swept volume of 5883 cc. Priced at £500, it was the largest car ever built by Vulcan.

By the end of 1907, all the cars had acquired high and low tension dual ignition, shaft drive was standard throughout the range, and the larger models had four-speed gearboxes.

A new 12 hp model appeared in 1909, and was

Right: a 1904 twin-cylinder 10 hp seen on the London to Brighton run in 1963

Below: a 1914 10/15 hp

Above: a 1922 10 hp

Right: this 1921 car had a four-cylinder engine of 3686 cc

apparently such a success that it was followed in mid-1910 by a version of 15.9 hp and 2412 cc. Commented *The Autocar*: 'For accessibility and simplicity, soundness of material and honesty of workmanship, this Vulcan equalled, if it did not excel, the preceding members of its family.' In common with other models in the range, this new Vulcan had unit construction of engine and gearbox, the unit being three-point-suspended in the frame, and an interesting detail was the use of shell big-end bearings at a time when most big-ends were metalled directly in the rod. This was, apparently, because a large proportion of Vulcan output was exported to the colonies, far away from repair establishments. Added *The Autocar*: 'All the Vulcan chassis are subjected to severe test runs over the Yorkshire hills before they leave the works. From examination of the processes and work on more than one occasion we are bound to say that the Vulcan cars are second to none at the price on the market today. They have proved eminently satisfactory in the hands of private owners.'

In 1913 a 15–20 hp model was announced, with a monobloc engine of 3016 cc, four speeds forward and worm final drive. By now, Vulcan cars had bull-nosed radiators; electric lighting and detachable wheels were available as part of an 'option pack' costing £25. At this time the 15.9 model cost £350, the 15/20 hp £400.

There was to have been a $1\frac{1}{2}$ litre model, the Vulcanette, with electric lighting and starting for 1915, but World War I intervened.

Post-war production was overshadowed by the truck side of the company's activities, but the car range initially concentrated on the Vulcan 20 hp, 16 hp, and the 12, though some uncharacteristic experiments were also carried out with V8 and sleeve-valve engines, none of which ever appear to have reached the public. At this period the company was operating on the fringes of the Harper-Bean group, though this arrangement short, if costly, duration.

To judge from a reader's letter in *Autocar* in 1922, these post-war Vulcans were somewhat heavy and lethargic; the 16 hp was only capable of 48 mph, at which speed it became 'somewhat unsteady', and reported a petrol consumption of 13–20 mpg.

But a 12 hp, carrying four passengers, achieved some kind of an endurance record on 25 April 1923, by making 53 consecutive ascents of the 1:3.9 gradient of Sutton Bank, in Yorkshire: 'This performance is equivalent,' claimed Vulcan, 'to a total climb of over 50,000 ft, or almost TWICE THE HEIGHT OF MOUNT EVEREST.' The performance was especially meritorious in view of the fact that the car was completely standard, having been taken from a Liverpool showrooms the previous evening, and driven to Sutton Bank overnight.

It was in 1923 that C. B. Wardman organised a partial merger of Vulcan with Lea-Francis, and certain models produced by the two marques, like the Early Christians, had all things in common. Like the unreliable twin ohc engine of the 1927 line-up; designed by A. O. Lord, this six-cylinder unit powered the new 14/40 Vulcan in 1.7 litre form, and was increased in capacity for 1928 to 2 litres, thus creating the 16/60, which was available with full-width fabric 'Gainsborough' coachwork of supreme hideousness.

Fortunately, this horrid machine was the last of the Vulcan cars; thereafter the Southport firm concentrated on its excellent lorries, eventually amalgamating with Tilling-Stevens of Maidstone, and thus ultimately with the Rootes Group, which discontinued the marque in 1953.   DBW

A famous driver from the heroic age

LOUIS WAGNER, born in Paris in 1882, was one of the most famous drivers of the 'heroic age' of motor racing. Wagner joined the racing department of Darracq at Suresnes in 1901, and became a team driver in 1903.

Alexandre Darracq believed in entering his racing cars in as many speed events as possible, and throughout the 1903 season, Wagner was fully occupied with races, hill-climbs and sprints. He won the Circuit of Bastogne, and was lying third in the voiturette class of Paris-Madrid when it was halted at Bordeaux.

Wagner crossed the Atlantic in 1906 to compete in the Vanderbilt Cup: he won, after a hard-fought race, and it was reported that he could have gone even faster had it not been for the crowds swarming onto the track. He did indulge his taste for speed during his visit, however, with a quick burst down Broadway, which so scandalised the local constabulary that they clapped him into New York's Tombs prison for 48 hours!

Mechanical failure spoiled the Darracq chances in the 1907 Targa Florio, when Wagner and Hanriot were forced to retire with broken half-shafts: Alexandre Darracq blandly announced that he was going to attribute the breakages to the carelessness of the drivers, who must surely have run off the road. Angered by this slander, Wagner stormed off to offer his services to FIAT, who agreed to repay the bond linking him to the Darracq company, and to take him on at double the appearance money, as well as guaranteeing him starts in more major races.

Alexandre Darracq, who does not appear to have been a particularly likeable character, protested, and threatened to take the case before the French government; he wasn't going to have one of his leading drivers walking out to join a foreign rival company! However, his threats proved impotent, and by the next major race, the Kaiserpreis, Wagner was a member of the FIAT team, along with Nazzaro and Lancia.

But Nazzaro won the Kaiserpreis; and he won the 1907 French Grand Prix, too, though Wagner led for the first two laps until a broken camshaft caused his retirement.

The 1908 Grand Prix saw *all* the Fiats eliminated by the end of the fourth lap, but to compensate for this Wagner carried off the American Grand Prize at Savannah.

In 1909, with Grand Prix racing temporarily in abeyance, Wagner switched his attention to flying, and joined the aircraft manufacturing company formed by his erstwhile team-mate Hanriot; he was a participant at many of the early flying meetings, and was actually airborne at the 1910 Bournemouth event when C. S. Rolls crashed with fatal results in his Wright Flyer.

The 1912 French Grand Prix saw the swansong of the monster racing cars, with Wagner, De Palma and Bruce Brown driving Fiats with engines displacing over 14 litres: at the end of the first day's racing, Wagner was lying third, despite recurrent tyre trouble: he finished in second place, behind George Boillot's Peugeot.

Wagner elected to drive for Mercedes in the 1914 French Grand Prix—Fiat, it is said, realis-

Above: Wagner poses for the camera in Lyon in the cockpit of his 1914 GP Mercedes

ing that their new GP cars were insufficiently developed to stand a chance, sportingly offered to let Wagner transfer his allegiance to the German marque. He finished second, behind the sister car of Christian Lautenschlager.

Back with Fiat after the war, Wagner competed in the 1921 Brescia Grand Prix, but was slowed to third by tyre trouble.

He joined Ballot that season, finishing seventh in the 1921 French Grand Prix on a straight-eight of that marque; the following year he took part in the Grand Prix in a Rolland-Pilain, but failed to last the race out. In 1924 he was driving for Alfa Romeo; in 1925 he was with Delage, Peugeot and Ariès as a freelance.

The 1926 season saw a sixth place in the Targa Florio and a second place in the Coppa Florio, on a sleeve-valve Peugeot, while 1927 found Wagner at the wheel of a Talbot, in which he made a record lap in the French Grand Prix, despite mechanical troubles. Then, after almost a quarter of a century in motor racing, Wagner retired from international competition.

After World War II, tuberculosis of the bone compelled the amputation of a leg, and Wagner was given the post of instructor and supervisor at the Montlhéry circuit: but the disease worsened, and by the late 1950s he was housebound. Wagner died in 1960, and was buried at Montlhéry.   DBW

This magnificent four-color encyclopedia is brought to you by Columbia House

in cooperation with Orbis Publishing Ltd., one of Great Britain's most enterprising publishers.

Rather than change any of the encylopedia's authoritative international automotive text, we have

included a glossary of terms that will give you immediate American equivalents, a conversion table

for the international metric system, and a conversion table for equivalent monetary values.

Glossary

BRITISH	AMERICAN
Aerial	Antenna
Aluminium	Aluminum
Apron	Skirt
Big-end	Rod (conrod) bearing
Blower *(colloquial)*	Supercharger
Bonnet	Hood
Boot	Trunk
Brake servo	Power brake
Bulkhead	Firewall
Capacity	Displacement
Carburetter; carburettor	Carburetor
Check strap	Door stop
Clutch release bearing	Clutch throwout bearing
Control box	Voltage regulator
Crown wheel and pinion	Ring gear and pinion
Cylinder block	Cylinder crankcase
Dip switch	Dimmer switch
Door pillar	Door post
Drop arm	Pitman arm
Drop-head	Convertible
Dynamo	Generator
Epicylic gearbox	Planetary gearbox
Exhaust silencer	Muffler
Facia panel	Dashboard
Gear lever	Gear shift lever
Gearbox	Transmission
Gearbox housing	Transmission casing
Gearchange	Gearshift
Glassfibre	Fiberglass
Grease nipple	Grease fitting
Gudgeon pin	Piston or wrist pin
Half shaft	Axle shaft
Handbrake	Parking brake
Hose clip	Hose clamp
Ignition harness	Ignition set
Kerb	Curb
Layshaft	Counter shaft
Main shaft	Output shaft
Marque	Brand, make

BRITISH	AMERICAN
Motor	Engine
Number plate	License plate
Overrider	Bumper guard
Paraffin	Kerosene
Parking brake	Parking lock
Petrol	Gasoline, ''gas''
Petrol pump	Gasoline or fuel pump
Production car	Stock car
Propellor shaft	Drive shaft
Quarter light	Door vent
Rear lamp	Tail light
Rear seat squab	Rear setback or backrest
Reverse lamp	Back up light
Roof lamp	Dome light
Saloon	Sedan
Scuttle	Cowl
Selector rod	Shift bar
Servo-assisted	Power assisted
Side lamp	Parking light
Side member	Side rail
Spanner	Wrench
Sparking plug	Spark plug
Starting handle	Crank handle
Steering column	Steering post
Steering relay	Steering idler
Stub axle	Steering knuckle
Sump	Pan
Swivel pin	King pin
Toe board	Toe pan
Track	Tread
Track rod	Tie bar or track bar
Two-stroke	Two-cycle
Tyre	Tire
Valance	Rocker panel
Wheel arch	Wheelhouse or housing
Wheel brace	Wheel wrench
Windscreen	Windshield
Wing	Fender
Wishbone	A-arm; Control arm
Works	Plant, factory

Metric Equivalents
(Based on National Bureau of Standards)

Length

Centimeter (Cm.)	= 0.3937 in.	In.	= 2.5400 cm.
Meter (M.)	= 3.2808 ft.	Ft.	= 0.3048 m.
Meter	= 1.0936 yd.	Yd.	= 0.9144 m.
Kilometer (Km.)	= 0.6214 mile	Mile	= 1.6093 km.

Area

Sq. cm.	= 0.1550 sq. in.	Sq. in.	= 6.4516 sq. cm.
Sq. m.	= 10.7639 sq. ft.	Sq. ft.	= 0.0929 sq. m.
Sq. m.	= 1.1960 sq. yd.	Sq. yd.	= 0.8361 sq. m.
Hectare	= 2.4710 acres	Acre	= 0.4047 hectar
Sq. km.	= 0.3861 sq. mile	Sq. mile	= 2.5900 sq. km.

Volume

Cu. cm.	= 0.0610 cu. in.	Cu. in.	= 16.3872 cu. cm.
Cu. m.	= 35.3145 cu. ft.	Cu. ft.	= 0.0283 cu. m.
Cu. m.	= 1.3079 cu. yd.	Cu. yd.	= 0.7646 cu. m.

Capacity

Liter	= 61.0250 cu. in.	Cu. in.	= 0.0164 liter
Liter	= 0.0353 cu. ft.	Cu. ft.	= 28.3162 liters
Liter	= 0.2642 gal. (U.S.)	Gal.	= 3.7853 liters
Liter	= 0.0284 bu. (U.S.)	Bu.	= 35.2383 liters

Liter $= \begin{cases} 1000.027 \text{ cu. cm.} \\ 1.0567 \text{ qt. (liquid) or } 0.9081 \text{ qt. (dry)} \\ 2.2046 \text{ lb. of pure water at } 4\ \text{C} = 1 \text{ kg.} \end{cases}$

Weight

Gram. (Gm.)	= 15.4324 grains	Grain	= 0.0648 gm.
Gram	= 0.0353 oz.	Oz.	= 28.3495 gm.
Kilogram (Kg.)	= 2.2046 lb.	Lb.	= 0.4536 kg.
Kg.	= 0.0011 ton (sht.)	Ton (sht.)	= 907.1848 kg.
Ton (met.)	= 1.1023 ton (sht.)	Ton (sht.)	= 0.9072 ton (met.)
Ton (met.)	= 0.9842 ton (lg.)	Ton (lg.)	= 1.0160 ton (met.)

Pressure

1 kg. per sq. cm.	= 14.223 lb. per sq. in.
1 lb. per sq. in.	= 0.0703 kg. per sq. cm.
1 kg. per sq. m.	= 0.2048 lb. per sq. ft.
1 lb. per sq. ft.	= 4.8824 kg. per sq. m.
1 kg. per sq. cm.	= 0.9678 normal atmosphere

1 normal atmosphere $= \begin{cases} 1.0332 \text{ kg. per sq. cm.} \\ 1.0133 \text{ bars} \\ 14.696 \text{ lb. per sq. in.} \end{cases}$

Approximate Values of the Pound (£)
in terms of U.S. Dollars ($)

1914-1919	$4.76
1935	4.90
1936	4.97
1937	4.94
1938	4.89
1939	4.46
1940-1949	4.03
1950-1967	2.80
1968-1970	2.40
1971-1972	$2.40/2.60
1972-Present	2.60/2.10